AUTOMATION MANAGEMENT:
THE SOCIAL PERSPECTIVE

*Issues and responsibilities in
developing automation in the
public interest from the
viewpoints of industry, education,
labor and government.*

*Second Annual Symposium on Automation and Society co-sponsored by
the University of Georgia and Reliance Electric Company.*

SECOND ANNUAL GEORGIA-
RELIANCE SYMPOSIUM

AUTOMATION MANAGEMENT:
THE SOCIAL PERSPECTIVE

edited by

ELLIS L. SCOTT and ROGER W. BOLZ

published by

The Center for the Study of Automation and Society

Athens, Georgia

Preface

The papers in this book, prepared for the Second Annual Georgia-Reliance Symposium on Automation and Society, extend the thinking concerning the role of automation and society expressed during the first symposium in 1969. The 1970 Symposium focused on the problem of automation management, from a social perspective, as it relates to industry, education, labor and government.

It is recognized that automation technology has effect throughout the social structure. There are relationships between automation and other areas of technology, between automation and education, business and the economy and social organization. While recognized, these relationships have not been deeply probed, nor has there been adequate planning to assure that such relationships will have positive effect in the future.

The initial symposium indicated the need for an organization to encourage and aid the study of automation in relation to society on a systematic and continuing basis. The response has been the establishment of the Center for the Study of Automation and Society.

The first two symposia provided the groundwork for the continuing study of these phenomena. We must now move from the general and critical to the specific and constructive. Future symposia and related projects will be designed to extend, refine and apply the new thinking being done on the vital subject of automation.

William C. Flewellen, Jr.
Dean, College of Business Administration
University of Georgia

Vice-President and Secretary-Treasurer
Center for the Study of Automation and Society

Contents

1 Automation Management and the Public Interest 1
   Ellis L. Scott

2 Management of Automation: Some Reflections on Relevance . . 5
   George Kozmetsky

3 The Evolution of Automation 20
   Joseph Harrington, Jr.

4 Delusions of Grandeur or the Elusive Fruits of Automation . . . 32
   Herbert W. Robinson

5 Automation Management in Education 45
   Gordon B. Carson

6 Management of Data Automation 53
   Joseph B. Warren

7 The Planning Imperative 65
   Melvyn R. Copen

8 Some Manpower Implications 78
   Edgar Weinberg

9 Management Attitudes Toward Automation 92
   Russell A. Hedden

10 Implementing Automation 102
   John J. McNiff

11 Educational Institutions in an Age of Technological Change . . . 109
   Frederick L. Bates

12 Toward a Global Economy 118
   James C. Hetrick

13 Automation: Government's Role and Responsibility 126
   John E. Mock

14 Automation and Labor 138
   Ben B. Seligman

15 The Automation Environment 153
   K. Robert Hahn

16 Technical Innovation: Key to Economic and Social Development . 167
   Roger W. Bolz

Automation Management and the Public Interest

Ellis L. Scott

ADVANCED, SCIENCE-BASED TECHNOLOGIES such as automation are becoming increasingly relevant to all segments of social organization in today's societies. This relevance may vary among societies or among segments of a particular society. Nevertheless, there is increasing concern for the social implications of technology and one of the expressions of this interest was the 1970 Georgia-Reliance Symposium on Automation and Society. The particular emphasis here was placed on the respective roles and responsibilities of education, labor, industry and government. Time has reinforced the business and social imperatives for increased automation. Among these, as Hershner Cross[1] has pointed out:

"Inflation is a concept which today is understood by the most unsophisticated pensioner, not just economists and business men. We would all agree, of course, there are some things money can't buy — namely the things it bought last week.

"Foreign competition is a force we are feeling very keenly in several important sectors of the electrical industry. And so are many of our customers; those in the steel and marine industries for example.

"Galloping construction costs make it imperative for us and our customers to get the ultimate degree of productivity out of factory floor space.

"The mounting cost of materials compels us to work them smarter and to move them faster if we are to show the kinds of results in our annual reports that make a company's stock an attractive investment."

Better Information Needed

These factors have given business and industry a new stimulus — a new intensity and urgency to examine the need to automate and to consider the direction and speed it must take to insure business survival. These concerns expressed in the business community are increasingly expressed in labor, education and government. The magnitude of these decisions and their far-reaching consequences demand a better data base than we now have, more attention to long-range planning and effective implementation mechanisms throughout society.

Those persons who know automation technology in all its manifestations are aware that there exists an advanced technology of great sophistication and that it has already been applied in some fashion to almost all segments of society. These persons are also aware that, measured in terms of its potentiality, only the surface has been scratched and that we are really in the early stages of the utilization of automation. This positioning in the early phase of its application is a fortuitous circumstance — for it provides time to study, to plan and to implement so that automation's benefits may be achieved without the deleterious social consequences which might otherwise occur.

The future-oriented outlook has come into prominence in recent years. Planning has achieved a legitimacy and explicitness in society which it did not formerly possess. Technological and social forecasting are necessary if we are to anticipate the alternative futures and assess their consequences. There is no going back to a simpler way of life. Technology management must therefore develop as a concern for all segments of society. This confrontation must come head-on. Cross[1] tells the story about the fastidious housewife who was horrified to see a mouse scamper across her kitchen floor. Trembling, she sent her young son to the hardware store to buy some mousetraps. "But," she said, "for heaven's sake don't tell the clerk what we want them for."

The search for understanding of the nature of technology and its social implications may be expected to be difficult, frustrating, lonely and time-consuming. The experience of the first two symposia on automation and society demonstrated how much there is yet to know and how faltering and uncertain our present efforts to understand and control technology. Uncovering the issues expressed in the papers in this book is hopefully an important step toward specific and positive contributions to society.

Seeking Keys to Management

Automation is a technology which will affect people in many ways. Its effects may be judged on some scale of values as desirable or undesirable. The course of its implementation depends upon how these effects are perceived and evaluated by various segments of society. The question of management is not simply to avoid undesirable consequences but to develop a creative approach to it, as Dr. Kozmetsky has outlined in his paper. Technology-society relationships traverse scientific, technological and social domains. Technology-society issues emerge as expressions of concerns. These become structured as representations of the perceptual framework inherent within a societal frame of reference. Decisions are made on the basis of these "definitions of the situation."

If automation is to be developed in harmony with and for the benefit of society certain things must be done. We must better understand and apply the wealth of technology which is available. We must make the educational system more flexible in meeting a technological society's requirements. Above all, we must be imaginative in visualizing social changes which lie ahead and in creating new social organizations and practices in harmony with these changes.

The key to effective management of technological change is social change. But this action framework involves the adequacy of our knowledge base, the effectiveness of planning, and the distribution of responsibilities within society. The definition and allocation of social obligations may be called the "ticklish question" issue. Tender and sensitive relationships are involved. Traditional establishments tend to be closed-systems — inner-directed entities. Technological change requires these systems to become increasingly other directed and who these others are becomes very important in determining the effects of technology on society.

One response to the need for automation management has been the development of system engineering and the larger systems approach. This orientation stresses the interrelationships of component elements and how the totality functions to serve stated objectives. It stresses input-output relationships and the whole viewed in terms of the environment in which the system functions. It is a mistake to think of automation as a technology in which man is engineered out of the system and need not be considered as an element in the system. In automation, regardless of the changing role of man or his remoteness from operations, we are still involved with man-machine relationships as a significant aspect of the technology.

Morris Tanenbaum[2] writing in Bell Telephone Magazine raises several crucial questions: "Will small modifications in our present guides be adequate to encourage technological innovation in the directions we wish for the future? If not, what new kinds of guides will be required? How will these new guides be developed? And how will the new guides interact with the established ecology of technological innovation?"

The program orientation of the Center for the Study of Automation and Society proposes to explore these questions along lines so as to:

Encourage and develop resources for planning and analysis.

Disseminate general knowledge of automation as a technology and its social implications.

Supply specific data needed for planning and decision-making.

Develop actual working relationships among industry, labor, education and government.

Involve professional resources of universities, corporations, unions and government agencies.

Explore applications of automation for economic development within and among nations.

Study the environmental impact of automation as a technology.

The contributions of the authors of this volume constitute a significant step in program development for Automation and Society.

REFERENCES
1. Cross, Hershner, *Tomorrow's Factory: Perspectives on Automation,* address to the 25th Annual Design Engineering Conference, Cleveland, Ohio, March 5, 1969.
2. Tanenbaum, Morris, "A Booming Technology, A Better Environment: Can We Have Both?", *Bell Telephone Magazine,* Fall 1970.

2

Management of Automation: Some Reflections on Relevance

George Kozmetsky

THE FORTHCOMING CREATIVE DECADE of the 1970s can be one in which coordination of all segments of automation and society takes place. In this respect, managers of automation will be required to synthesize scientific and technological changes on a national and worldwide basis, together with proper economic development for purposive human use of our nation and world work force. These changes, of course, must be based on the required societal reflections of individual and social values that are adaptable to changing cultural environments which fulfill for mankind and the individual an enriched life based on satisfaction and meaningful renewal.

The foregoing does point out that managers of automation can construct, fashion and idealize the scope and necessary detail of a meaningful techno-socio-economic-cultural era. Such an era must be constructed by managers of all of our institutions who view them as an organic whole. It is appropriate to project ourselves into the year 2001 in order to visualize the kind of era which will exist.

Undoubtedly automation practices in the year 2001 will be the result of applying current advances in research rather than depending on startling unpredictable breakthroughs. It is possible to make a number of useful generalizations concerning the exciting era of automation.

Cause and Effect Relationship

It is basic to the thesis of this paper that effects are produced by causes which were themselves the effects of earlier causes. Dr. Daniel J. Boorstin called such a generalization "a self-liquidating ideal"; in other words, an ideal disappears in the very act of fulfillment. He used the following example to illustrate his point:

"Henry Ford's dream was to make a new and better kind of family horse — a car which everybody could afford and which would last forever. Essential to his plan, of course, was perfecting his Model T. Although he was experimental in developing his car, he believed that once the design was fixed, the object was simply to find ways to make it by the millions. It was essential to his ideal that all the cars should be alike. As he saw it, mass production (what he called "the democratization of the auto-mobile") required standardization, and standardization meant turning out a single uniform product by the millions . . .

"To Ford this meant finding ways to turn out millions of Model T's. He was confident that he could succeed. In 1909 a friend warned Ford that the automobile would create a "social problem" by frightening all the horses on the highway. "No, my friend," Ford replied, "You're mistaken. I'm not creating a social problem at all. I am going to democratize the automobile. When I'm through everybody will be able to afford one, and about everyone will have one. The horse will have disappeared from our highways, the automobile will be taken for granted, and there won't be any problem."

"Ironically, his faith in the Model T was an Old World faith. His belief in the perfectible product rather than the novel product, his insistence on craftsmanship and function rather than on consumer appeal eventually left him behind. His genius had heralded a new age beyond his imaginings — and not at all to his taste.

"The effort to democratize the automobile proved self-defeating — and illustrated the problem of self-liquidating ideals."

Let us predict in the context of self-liquidating ideals the changing nature of automation in the year 2001 and its impact on: (1) The individual; (2) science and technology; (3) the corporation.

Automation and the Individual

By the year 2001, the management of automation can provide the individual the means to manage its own affairs to achieve the goals of: (1) Increased standard of living through automated production; (2) increased satisfaction in leisure time through modifying his institutions; (3) increased longevity through research.

It is possible to conceive of a simple flow diagram that encompasses the means of production, the structure of the social institutions and the efforts of research. (See Figure 1). In these endeavors to satisfy himself the individual is limited by a fixed amount of time and energy which he can expend daily; the real contribution of automation is to permit a shift of the amount of these limited commodities, time and energy, from maintaining a desired standard of living, to other needs, by reducing the time and energy required for what we look upon as "work."

One of the difficulties for managers is that the human energy required by the means of production has decreased considerably, but the time required has not decreased to the same extent. As a result he works long hours but is under exercised, resulting in heart attacks and other disorders for which he does not have sufficient time to correct through proper physical use of his muscular system and for which the "easy" nature of his white collar job is a detriment. As time becomes more available to invest in leisure pursuits, some of these pleasures will no doubt be directed towards correcting this flaw. Thus automation takes away the physical labor, but will eventually provide adequate time for muscular exercise in leisure activities.

An optimum distribution of time and energy among the principal goals of man is a problem for management and automation. The shift of time and effort among the choices is both individual and societal.

Individually most of us are well aware of the fact that we do this. We consciously shift our efforts between increasing our standard of living, seeking leisure, and providing for our longevity. Societally this occurrence

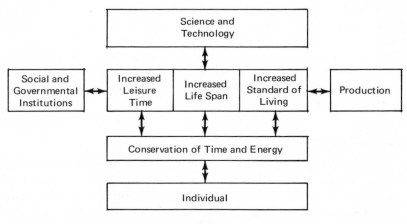

FIGURE 1.

is a natural consequence of the fact that we do it individually. That is one spends a certain amount of time attempting to increase his life span, therefore, he will surely pay to have some people study this problem full time. Hence, a statistical distribution of people exist who are involved in these areas and there is a shift in the total effort in these areas resulting from automation of the means of production.

Now this statistical effort is itself overseen by a larger "feedback" system managed by the U.S. Government. This system is also a product of management and automation whose function is to: (1) Prevent war or open external conflict among humans; (2) prevent economic chaos or poor management of national resources; (3) prevent social disorder or conflict of an internal nature among humans.

The government achieves this set of preventions, as best it can, through the automated use of good management planning. By the year 2001, it will understand these phenomena and have achieved some control over them through improved prediction methodology. The "horizons" of humans will be expanded greatly from insight gained through the availability of time and resources provided through the use of management planning, and automation to implement the planning. This insight will occur in the automation and management process itself, as well as in other areas.

The accumulation of knowledge or expansion of horizons generally follows the sequence: (1) How do things work?; (2) what are they made of?

This has been the trend in medicine, engineering and in the humanities. In medicine, and biology in general, we have discovered more or less how living things work and how to change their workings but we do not know what life is yet. In engineering, we have been making things for centuries but only lately have we discovered what things are made of — the atom and its parts. In the humanities, we have organized into groups and managed the affairs of groups for centuries but only lately are we learning what the human is like.

Automation and Science-Technology

Automation in the year 2001 will require a continuing and expanding science and technology. However, it must be purposive as contrasted to chance. By purposive, we mean that science and technology are related to a requirement of an organic system. In the past, technology took the results of prior scientific research and used them in engineering new or improved products. The prior research in most cases was the result of individual research either in industry or in the universities or by independent inventors. A common notion, still misunderstood and still prevalent in many circles was that research utilization would come long after their first conception and reduction to practice. There will always be room for such research results and researchers. However, there is increasing need and recognition that research must be directed towards solution of problems within a short period of time — 5, 10, 30, 50 years.

Since World War II there have literally been billions of dollars spent on research for defense, nuclear energy, and health care. It may be appropriate at this time to summarize a few general principles to be learned from the experience of such research.

The first principle is that with sufficient scientific research and technological development resources it is possible to create new industries that involve all segments of society. The critical factor is the decision to allocate the resources. For example, the investment of billions of dollars and the assignment of highly selected skilled personnel to the Manhattan Project gave rise to the atomic and nuclear bombs. The same results are evident in supersonic aircraft, reliable and high-speed digital electronic computers, spaceships, satellites for communication and weather forecasting. The resources required included not only highly capable scientific personnel, but high quality engineering talent, management, production, skilled, semi-skilled and unskilled laborers. For example, federal and state resources to control water pollution could aggregate $50 billion in the next 10 years. This is 2-1/2 Apollo programs over an equivalent span of time.

A second generalization evident from the past experiences that it is possible to predict many research results. That is, the output of research can be predicted while it is not always possible to predict beforehand how the research will be accomplished.

A third generalization is that it is possible to relate predicted demand and supply for products to research efforts. There has been an increasing recognition of the state of art concept with risk evaluation. However, the full benefit is directly related to the ability to forecast "predicted demand."

There is need to extend our research further in this area just as for the discovery of newer principles or development of advance components of new equipments or systems. We lack a unified set of tools for system analysis, system effectiveness and cost effectiveness and systems management planning and control. While there is extensive effort being conducted in each of these areas, to date little has been done to unify this overall area in terms of methodology or general principles.

A useful starting point to establish the basis from which scientific and technological predictions will be made is found by examining trends of the past two decades. Twenty-five years ago the United States had entered the postwar period of the mid-40's. The techniques and electronic devices used for purposes of war were being studied for peacetime applications. It was found that servomechanisms formerly used to direct antiaircraft guns could be used for industrial controls — material handling, positioning of machine tools and semiautomatic process sequencing. Radar was being studied as a telephone link of high capacity. A newcomer at that time on the scene, the digital computer could provide a means to mechanize complex manipulative and control problems associated with automation.

By the 1960's it turned out that it was not enough to merely recognize that elements of industry could be broken into the parts of a closed-loop control system such as structural units, sensor units, commutation units, actuator units and visual displays. It became apparent that any organic system, of which industry is one type, operated by virtue of something other than just simple feedback. Organic systems had to be examined in terms of the reasons for the functioning of the system. While these principles were set forth by Norbert Wiener in 1948, it took a number of military and nonmilitary systems applications to outline the practical problems of implementation.

Organic systems are characterized as manifesting in the broadest sense a form of intelligence. As such their basic building blocks are people, machines and their respective interfaces. How these elements are interrelated has been a continuous effort of study on the part of those working on complex systems projects. Most recently, attention has turned to the problem of considering the interrelations between multiple weapon systems which must function in close coordination with each other. Here the problem is not one of optimizing any one system, but designing sets of weapon systems which adequately assure our national defense posture. Such problems are still prevalent in attacking pollution, crime, poverty, and organization. By the year 2001, such solutions will be largely derived from the results of advance research being conducted today in the area of the management of automation.

Automation and the Corporation

Just as man himself undergoes daily change so it should be assumed that the corporation of year 2001 will be different in its appearance when compared with its image of today. Moreover, not only will the external appearance be altered but change will assert itself in all aspects of corporate existence from the macroscopic down to the minutia. History provides us with the lesson of change. Not one single system of man's making has remained unaltered down through the passage of time.

Industrialization and the growth of the corporate concept is of man's own making. It has constantly evolved and has never been static in its nature. Time is change. Corporate management establishing policy can either orient a company toward growth or collapse by recognizing the need for change as natural consequence of the passage of time or they can try to stop change occurring in the world about them.

Stated in another way, if we view the corporation of 2001 as to its' effects then it is possible to find that many of the causes for these effects are in operation today. To illustrate this point let us indicate as an effect the fact that automated industry in 2001 will use electrical power as the primary energy source. "Well that is obvious," everyone will say. Our concern is not with the obvious nature of that statement but rather with why it is obvious. The answer to this question is not as simple.

Let us attempt to show why causes obvious to us now lead to the foregoing conclusion. First, we are living today in a technological world that runs on electricity. Most of the energy and effort expended by our best minds are completely oriented toward this intuitive approach. An electrical motor designer would not devote effort to the development of a new type of motor that is driven by some as yet undiscovered energy source without being considered somewhat touched in the head and most certainly a very poor business man. To the contrary he will encourage efforts along these lines as being ridiculous unless someone else has already come up with the new source of energy whereupon the new motor design is removed from that category to one of merely risky business.

Attention must now be turned to the developer of the new power source. Present interest in industrial power lies with those whose business it is to produce and deliver industrial power. Efforts in these areas are concentrated on improving the operation of the existing systems and are not concerned with developing techniques which, for example, would make obsolete the huge investments in power plants and transmission lines presently used. We can expect changes in how electricity will be generated (nuclear reactors versus organically fueled generating stations), but not in terms of the kind of power that will be used by industry. If we were attempting to predict occurrences in the year 3001 instead of 2001 our present view of causes would not allow us to predict at this level of detail but would rather require that much larger concepts be dealt with whose causes lie in the present.

To study the corporation of the future is to study the manager of the future. To understand the ways in which corporations will operate we must examine the nature of the corporate policy of 2001. Causes can be established by referring to the area of corporate motivation.

Corporate policy in the area of motive is found by examining the motives of the managers of the corporation. In most cases, one man can be found who is dominant in that the company expresses his point of view. What are his motives? On the surface we can cite such obvious statements as profit motive (he wants to make a lot of money); social responsibility (he wants to lead man toward a better way of life); social recognition (he wants acceptance from the society by which he feels rejected); power (he wants to alter society so that it is more to his liking); establish a dynasty (he wants to build a perpetuating monument to himself); self-expression (he wishes to create and communicate something of himself to others). Before we too harshly criticize managers because they exhibit human characteristics, let us remember that we are all managers of something at sometime or another and pattern our lives after those who have achieved prominence in the practice of leadership.

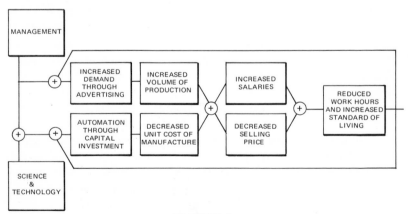

FIGURE 2.

In the year 2001 individual motivation or the seeking of satisfaction of basic needs for the individual will not be any different than it is today. Changes that we might expect will occur in the area of methods which are available for the expression of this need. Whereas in the past the range of individual expression available to the manager was rather narrow and centered about areas of profit motive and the increase of power and control, the trend for future corporate policy as assigned by management will broaden to allow expression in areas of government and education as well as those presently connected with industrial management. The manager of the future will find his activities extending across all three of these forementioned areas. Because of his special training he will be called upon from time to time to assist in establishing university curricula and suggesting the trends developing out of industrial need.

The role of the government as a stabilizing influence on the automated industrial system of 2001 will require his participation and contribution of specialized knowledge in this sphere to insure that the government's view of the industrial system is or contains a full understanding of the problems in which legislation and judicial interpretation will be made. Because of this greater range of expression available to the manager of the year 2001 we should expect his policy making motivation as regards the industrial portion of his total activity to be altered from what it is today. He will be reflecting his interest and concern in governmental problems, in educational problems, in the nature and structuring of the organization that he is responsible for.

The Nature of Automation

Let us now turn our attention to the criterion by which society will judge automation as successful or not. The degree of leisure available and the increase in the standard of living achieved, I believe will be the deciding factor. From the diagram shown in Figure 2, I have attempted to illustrate the self-correcting nature of automated industry. Automation will be judged mainly by the extent that a product achieves the above mentioned criterion, namely; the relation of management and automation in a manner which increase meaningful demand that leads to an increased volume of production coupled with automation through capital investments that lead to decreased unit costs which in turn results in decreased selling prices and increased salaries that raises the standard of living and increased leisure time.

The nature of automated industry can be implied as follows: (1) Automation will lead to a condition of stable growth of the economy; (2) a growing tendency for industry to centralize by product line will result; (3) an overall increase in scientific methods will be used in motivating demand from the inception of the product to its final consumption.

A degree of management within all of our socio-techno-economic-cultural institutions will be needed that exceeds any presently employed method of operation. In short, management by the principle of exception will not work because of the increased tempo due to automation in all segments of our society. Misalignment of a major policy cannot be tolerated and could lead generally to catastrophy.

Any organization requires from management a purpose or direction. Establishment of policy cannot be automated. Policy must include direction of growth as well as the impetus or magnitude of the forces compelling that growth. Within the main decision-making structure there exist suborganizations, each of which carry out a portion of the overall policy. All subpolicy must be brought into alignment with the overall policy of the company if directed growth is to be maintained.

It now becomes possible to note where the management-automation interface will always be; namely, at a level in the organization below which functions and policy are executed solely by means of automatic control devices and above which are found humans. At this interface, we find individuals who are responsible for functions that prior to the introduction of automation were performed by people. The supervisor at the automation interface has the task of ascertaining that the automatic equipment is capable of implementing subpolicy required at his level of the organization. Furthermore, the supervisor at the automation interface must be concerned with defining his own position so that a gradual assimilation of these functions by the automated portion of the industry can come about. His natural apprehension for replacing himself will be eliminated if the management level above him provides the training necessary to insure his moving up to a new job as soon as he brings the level of automation up to his present activity.

The Future

At this point it is appropriate to discuss the philosophical context within which all managers of automation will manage. The techno-socio-economic and cultural society of the future, e.g., 2001, will be based in my opinion on capitalism. However, it will be transformed.

The economic and political success of the United States has been in part due to its "traditional 'capitalistic' (and democratic) factors as sufficient flexibility to accommodate entrepreneurship and a fundamental belief in the value of individual initiative and free competition."[1] Capitalism as a philosophy has gone through at least several phases in the United States. The famous business historian, Professor Norman De Gras, had delineated these phases in terms of "financial capitalism" to outside the United States and, in later times, on internal private financial institutions in the United States. The shortcomings of "financial capitalism" led to what many of us lived through as the "Great Depression." The second period was more of a reliance upon federal sources for financing or government guarantees and extensive use of a dramatic partnership between the federal government and private enterprise to prevent the "scourge of depression." The successes of "national capitalism" has made our nation economically affluent and thrust it into the forefront of world political powers.

Success at a national level too often, as at a personal level, lays the seeds for unforeseen possible problems. Today it is clear that "national capitalism" has been deficient in two respects. The first of these is that it has resulted in the United States' creating and consuming from 40 to 60 percent of the total world wealth with only 6 percent of the total population. The second is that national capitalism has, by its very success, dulled our ability to react to the existence − and their timely prevention within the nation − of underprivileged classes, urban crises, pollution, crime, a rising group of lost youths, an emerging new left, and insufficient regard to our more rural areas and their transitional problems into tomorrow's industrial society. In short then, the deficiencies of national capitalism have created the need for what I call "creative capitalism" based on innovative private management.

The task that the last third of the 20th century industrial state imposes on our society is the increasing development of people for nonroutine tasks under "creative capitalism". Particularly since World War II we have seen the rise in what we could call the technological industry, which is concerned with "nonroutimized" kinds of problems and demands that require a new order of solution. These problems are concerned with space exploitation, building of megalopolises, control of environment, water pollution, marine sciences, crime, transportation, and environmental health.

These areas provide the bases for an expanding nonroutine industry of the next "decade or two." On the other hand, the innovative management is aware that the problems of the second industrial revolution also provide opportunities. Cybernetics as a science has yet to clearly delineate and specify these opportunities and problems. What are some of these yet unexposed problems that only man can identify?

1. What will be the nature of the 21st century industries in the United States? How will their development be financed? What will be their markets?

2. Leisure as an industry is not only in its infancy but is not yet clearly delineated. During the transition to the 21st century, there will be four types of leisure to satisfy the following groups: First, the unemployed (waiting between jobs); second, the low-salaried employees working short hours; third, the higher salaried groups working short hours; and fourth, the professionals (including statesmen) working long hours and who will have limited leisure in sporadic bursts.

3. When will a black cease being a black?

4. How do you redistribute the wealth under "creative capitalism"?

5. How do you allocate abundant resources — short run, long run?

6. How will new forms of organizations change the institutions to fit the social and individual needs?

Our society does not realize that our intellectual resources are in short supply. Furthermore, the scarcity of intellectual resources is not only recognized by industry and government, but there is an awareness that their supply is relatively inelastic.

In short, technological change has set up a self-amplifying system in its demands for intellectual resources. Technology generates new advancements which, in turn, generate still greater need for sophisticated intelligence. The task for management education is not merely to select the gifted or excellent student for training but to develop on a broad front all levels of skills to meet the requirements of society in developing people for all their roles in the society and which are essential for the full cultivation of each individual's talents and abilities.

The problem for managers of automation is to develop innovations which result in intelligent action to solve the cummulative consequences of continuing rapid technological change, economic growth, urbanization, and continuing deescalation of rural areas in a way that provides for a renewed democratic society in the context of "creative capitalism." Another way of saying this is to repeat the late President John F.

Kennedy's call in his inaugural address to confront the "unfinished business of our generation." Rhetoric alone cannot solve these problems. Nor may it be possible for any one of our 19th century institutions to solve these problems alone. The 1950s and 1960s saw the growth of a new complex that was instrumental in solving many of our defense, space, and nuclear energy national problems; namely, the Federal government, the university, and private enterprise complexes. Their potential problems were clearly stated by the late President D. Eisenhower in his farewell address. The 1970s and 1980s could well see the rise of a broader set of complexes which would include not only the federal government but also local government entities; not only universities but also graduate centers; not only private enterprises as represented in the urban home offices and plants but also in their local plants found in the rural areas, supplemented by emerging new firms that utilize the local resources relative to the economic utilization of advanced technology. In many respects, "creative capitalism" can well be institutionalized on these more broadly-based complexes.

It is my opinion that the so-called new left of today has become old and obsolete even before it has become effective. They, like Don Quixote, are jousting with problems created by a capitalism of the past. Their ideas of capitalism are those before the depression. Creative capitalism must advance our society beyond the need for imperialism or exploitation of people. Creative capitalism's success depends on its creation of wealth in a manner that truly establishes the community of humanity as the goal of our society which all true leaders throughout the world are seeking today. Wealth produced under creative capitalism must be distributed in a manner which makes it possible to increase the standard of living of all the people in the world. The new institutions or complexes upon which creative capitalism is based will make it possible to solve, on a timely basis, our social problems simultaneously while creating wealth and providing for meaningful leisure for all people in the world.

What then should we expect from managers of automation for the emerging era of creative capitalism? The era of transition to the expansion of our nonroutine industry can glean significant lessons from the ecstasy and agony that all segments of our society faced in the 1960s. The first lesson is: one must have pride in self. Many hippies do not have pride in self. That is why they have a tendency to move toward demoralization — emotional and physical. They are, in truth, escaping from self. On the other hand, the negro, through "black power" and "black is beautiful," is on the first rungs of pride in self. Professional people attain pride in self through their educational avenues and their accomplishments within their social or cultural institutions – yes, even their companies.

The second lesson is: when a human being, regardless of race, has pride in self, his need to seek avenues to man's inhumanity to man naturally diminishes. Black power and white supremacy questions become less significant or even an enduring issue.

The third lesson is: as the transition era progresses from pride in self (in other words, with self-confidence) and one turns toward man's humanity to man, the whole rate of positive and meaningful progress accelerates exponentially. As each man clearly sees his role in the new era of social stability, the minority lines as well as intellectual and religious lines disappear. Then the true community of humanity becomes the foundation of and remains as a lasting heritage to the coming generations who follow.

The final rung in the progress of man's humanity to man is that in every aspect man is human and imperfect. No simple or complex perfection is possible. This applied to every aspect of one's personal actions and the institutions which man forms. Therefore, the dedication of self to man's humanity to man requires an inner conviction based on patience and willingness to make necessary adjustments; above all a patience of high order to mitigate man's inhumanity to man through spontaneous or responsible emotional personal behavior or professional behavior.

The insurrectionists of the 1970's are equally dedicated to their belief of achievement of utopia through destruction of today's institutions. They in effect are too often exploiting the lesser flaws of today's and yesterday's institutions without due regard to their benefits nor the lasting results of their irresponsible behavior used in their destruction. Their amplification of minor flaws are no better than other practices of man's inhumanity to man. Man's inhumanity to man under any guise is still barbarism. Barbarism under any conditions and in any society is not an answer. Violence and retaliation are, in my opinion, not modern solutions they are decadent answers from the past.

Responsible actions cannot be performed in silence or in violence. Man's humanity to man as a goal of society will not come from either group. Man's humanity to man is not the creation of destruction or apathy. Confidence in self demands a quiet confrontation with those who are involved in violence or silence. An active confrontation that calls a halt to wanton destruction of self, property, and society. For such peaceful actions are demanded if one truly believes and is prepared to seek man's humanity to humanity. For, in fact, quiet nonviolence demands a vast majority. For only through sheer numbers can one proceed with the true goals of any society. Nonparticipation, silence, or merely on looking will not provide for diminishing the fear of man's inhumanity to man. Sheer numbers for nonviolence make possible the useful discrimination of peaceful means for change. Nonviolence can provide more meaningful change for right rather than change based on appeasement derived from violence or temper tantrums.

Let us focus for a moment on tomorrow's leadership for the community of humanity. Automation has forced yesterday's leadership to change if they are to be veritably tomorrow's leaders. There is no room in tomorrow's technology to make the lines of community wider or longer. Coexistence and respect for man's native and learned intelligence are man's future. Science and technology in truth are forcing man to examine if not accept the community of humanity even as they threaten today's stable economic, political, religious, and social orders. Then the true liberation of progress can begin. The community of humanity globally unites all peoples.

The creation of wealth equally demands responsible leadership for the community for humanity. Creative positive leadership and management cannot put off for any extended period a realistic discharge of their duties to accelerate towards a constructive community of humanity or to continue on a course of indecision that leads to man's inhumanity to man.

REFERENCES
1. Robin Marris, "The Role of the Business-Like Organization in the Technology of Social Change," *Social Innovation in the City*. Edited by R.S. Rosenbloom and R. Marris. Cambridge, Mass; Harvard University Press, 1969, p.2.

3

The Evolution of Automation

Joseph Harrington, Jr.

WHAT WILL BE THE ROLE of the manager of automation? The manager's training tells him to go back to the record of the past, examine it for its apparent characteristics and their trends. On this basis, the managers should be able to anticipate the future and be guided accordingly.

This is a dandy theory, but its execution is tough when the ground keeps shifting underneath. Automation today is not what it was 20, or ten or even two years ago. Automation is a very volatile subject. Automation is a young thing; managers can remember when automation was born, and can mentally review its entire life history of about two decades. And many testify to the "shifting sands" of this history.

Two of the students at the Institute of Advanced Studies at Princeton, New Jersey met on the campus on day. One of them asked, "How is that new course in subatomic particles coming along?" The second replied, "It's a delightful course — everything we learned last week is now obsolete." They might well have been discussing automation.

In this paper, the author will: (1) Review the situation of 1950, of 1960, and of 1970 to support the author's thesis of change; (2) present a much longer perspective view to show there is a firm substrata in this field; (3) then, try a little extrapolation into the world of management of automation.

The Record of the Last Two Decades

In 1950, automation was the buzz word of the hour. It was common to characterize automation as the second Industrial Revolution. Automatic machinery was being designed to replace human skill and intelligence just as in the first Industrial Revolution, steam and water power replaced human physical labor. The high point of automation was the so-called Detroit Automation, particularly the huge in-line transfer machines which produced auto components in great numbers.

At that time, there was a tremendous pent-up demand for goods resulting from the austerity of the war years; and mass production was the answer to that demand. Furthermore, the war-born technologies of electronics, servomechanisms, and systems engineering were available to implement the automation. Professor Norbert Weiner predicted that technology had the competence to replace all human labor with machinery within ten years. This prediction, which is now so patently erroneous, produced a tremendous social unrest and concern as to the implications of automation for people and for society.

Mass production technology is characterized by high-cost machines with expensive and highly-specialized fixtures and cutters and long setup times; as a result, long runs are efficient which leads to large inventories and tends to stultify developmental changes in the product. In fact mass production means just more and more of the same thing; it must be aimed at the median of the mass taste which means mass mediocrity. It wasn't long before the public tired of this.

Things had changed radically by 1960. Numerical Control held the spotlight of the day. We heard very little about automation except as it applied to the intensive mechanization of many of our factories. There was a real reversal of all of the trends in this switch from automation to Numerical Control. While N/C still implies high cost fully automatic machinery, it has very little else in common with the traditional automation.

Its tools are universal as to the product they make and versatile as to the types of operations they perform. It is highly adaptable to short runs of parts, low cost cutting tools and fixtures and short setup times. This permits the collection of very small inventories and is a strong encouragement to customize the product for the individual consumer. There has been very little agonizing in the social and labor relations sense involved with the introduction of Numerical Control — perhaps because it was so complex a technology and took so long to introduce, it was done so carefully that the major pitfalls of the introduction of automation were avoided.

In 1970, another change in the buzz word of the day. N/C is now old hat and computer-assisted management control is the coming thing. In the short years since N/C was first introduced, it has changed from a specialized tool in the aerospace industries, to a generalized tool in machine shops, to a method of shop control in metalworking factories. And now Numerical Control coupled with computer-aided design and data processing for factory management is becoming an integral part in the total structure of computer-assisted management.

Today, society is on the verge of widespread application of computer-aided design in the product concept and development facets of our corporations. On the shop floor N/C equipment is being converted from tape control to on-line computer control. Adaptive control is being introduced and Numerical control is extended to many operations other than metal cutting activities.

All of these developments are tied together through the common use of data processing equipment and all have as their end object the improved management of the total business. The computer is an essential tool to the management of all portions of a modern corporation. Interestingly enough, there is absolutely no discussion of the social impact of this really revolutionary change. The subject has passed completely out of the range of comprehension or even awareness of the average person.

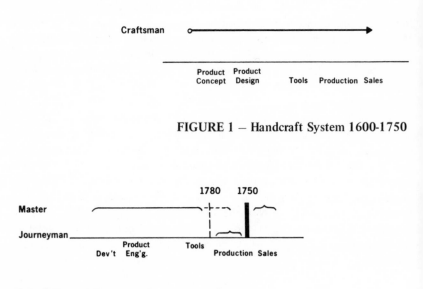

FIGURE 1 — Handcraft System 1600-1750

FIGURE 2 — Master and Journeyman Systems

Clearly, I believe that these three snapshots ten years apart substantiate the assertion that we are involved with a rapidly-shifting base when we use the word "automation." In fact, there may be considerable risk in even using the same word. But, certainly no one in his right mind would attempt to coin another one.

The Long-Range Perspective

The theme of this symposium is management of automation. This theme introduces a longer perspective view of the change in the concept of management in manufacturing in the United States. The purpose of this paper is to demonstrate the progressive fractionation of the management function and then its reintegration, a process just coming into play.

Figure 1 shows the span of control of an individual in the development of a product in the earlier stages of industrial history. In the colonial years, a craftsman not only conceived of the product and designed it, he made his own materials, made his own tools, fabricated the product, he even sold it from his kitchen or his barn. He was, in effect, a one-man factory. He was a watchmaker, a cabinetmaker, a gunsmith, or a shoemaker, but he

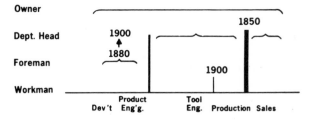

FIGURE 3 — Early Factory System

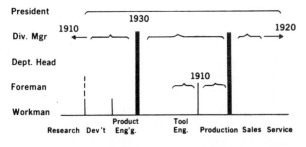

FIGURE 4 — Mass Production Systems

performed all of the operations from conception to distribution of the product. Variability was the hallmark of the handmade item as those of you who collect antique furniture are well aware.

When the demand for goods increased and one man's labor was not enough, our craftsman added a few journeymen workmen to assist him in the repetitive stages of his work and he spun off to a peddler or a shop-keeper the function of selling the finished product. He retained for himself the supervision of the entire production and the essential functions of inventing the product, designing it, developing the tools and the materials.

The dates which are shown in these diagrams are merely illustrative; there was, of course, no sharp point in time when these transitions were made. When in the early 1800s the steam engine and water power brought into being the factory, it was convenient to bring more and more people together in a single location − thus we see the multiplication of levels of command in the hierarchy, Figure 2.

Sometime after the Civil War, Figure 3, the function of developing new products was assigned to an inventive old "codger" who was kept in the back room to develop new products. Management separated the tool-makers from the tool users in the factory. The strengthening barrier was growing between the distribution or sales portion of the organization and the manufacturing portion.

Figure 4 shows the condition of the mass production industries in the early part of this century. Research people were separated from the development people, given white coats, and were put in a laboratory. Those who maintained the product in the field, were separated from those who sold the product in the field. And again, there emerged another couple of layers in the hierarchy of command. A strong barrier had grown up between the product development people and the production organization.

Figure 5 shows the culmination of this mass production technology with a great many levels in the hierarchy and a great many very strong lines dividing one function from another in all portions of the organization. There was specialization in the development and the product design engineers, and there was erected a new function of manufacturing engineering in the factory. These barriers were indeed high and strong. Communication was achieved only by going up and over the walls, even to Vice Presidential level.

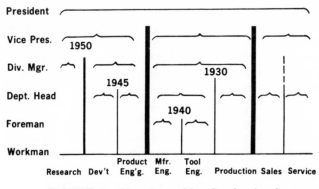

FIGURE 5 – Very Large Mass Production Systems

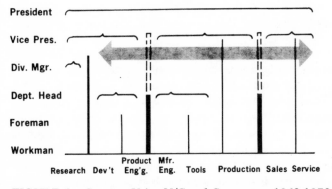

FIGURE 6 – Systems Using N/C and Computers 1960-1970

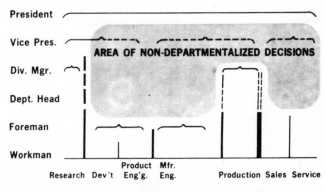

FIGURE 7 – Systems of the Future

Thus, for 150 years American industry taught our managerial people to confine themselves to the field of their assigned authority, to optimize their operation, and to report through channels. Cross-communication has not been overly encouraged. The advent of the computer and the numerically controlled tools has made a sudden change in this entire management structure.

No longer is it possible to consider the shape of a part and the making of a part and the use of a part as three separate subjects; they are all essentially one subject, Figure 6. No longer can our managers make independent, autocratic, and sequential decisions. Decisions must be made concurrently and harmoniously. As a result of the impact of this technology, our managers are having to do what the business school teachers have been preaching for years — reintegrate the management of manufacturing into a single function. Technology has perforated the barriers; down come the walls.

Figure 7 shows what the author believes will be the nature of the future organization. There will be a large area of nondepartmentalized decision-making, straddling the exact same span of control as did our original craftsmen in colonial days. This will not be done by a single person, but by a group of persons acting as an entity. This configuration raises questions about management's understanding of computers. Their mechanism is little understood; there is a mystique about the whole situation and it tends to be regarded with a great deal of awe and even superstition. This is a mistake; the computer is looked upon much as our forefathers looked upon steam — a sudden newcomer to the scene which radically changed the organization of the factory, the type of tools being used, and their management. The same thing has happened with the computer, yet today steam is a well-accepted servant of man. Management should regard the computer the same way. Similarly, managers must not be overawed by those who run the computer and their professional jargon. They, too, are servants and must be tamed. Now it seems that management can see the essential unity which has persisted throughout all of manufacturing history.

The Management of Manufacturing in the Future

Any way one looks at it, manufacturing can be seen as a single function. As these figures show, there is the continuity from the concept of the product through its design, development, engineering, production, marketing, and servicing. There is the continuity of activity from the purchase of materials, their fabrication, assembly, and distribution. Difficult as it is, management must abandon its old traditional schooling and look upon manufacturing of a product as a single function. Only then can management appreciate the full implication of new manufacturing technologies and take full advantage of them.

The emphasis and the interest in automation technology is swinging completely away from the individual machines and is focusing on systems of machines. Obviously, industry cannot have one without the other, but the solution of individual machine problems, mechanization, and automation have become fairly routine and the forward thinkers are directing their efforts to the system of machines which constitutes a productive unit.

The concern today with the systems of machines is not so much with the mechanization problems as with the managerial problems. If management ties all of its factory, in effect, into one great machine, then the managers had better be prepared to manage it. If management ties all the corporation into one great manufacturing machine from R & D clear through Marketing, then management had better be prepared to manage that corporation. Management has, perforce, been consolidated or integrated or reunited or refused into its original monolithic structure.

In October 1969 in Davenport, Iowa, the Department of Defense called together 700 of the best brains of the entire technology to discuss the problems of computer-aided manufacturing, computer-aided design, and Numerical Control. The state-of-the-art reports showed that on-line computers are being applied not only for fabrication of parts, but for testing them, assembling them, and moving them through the factory. When the computer can do all of these things, the machine knows all that the Superintendent needs to know and if the machine can be taught a few simple decision rules it will take care of all routine decisions. Furthermore, the machine will have the wits to signal for help when it finds a situation for which it has not been programmed; that's better than most junior managers will do.

The Davenport state-of-the-art reports also showed that computer-aided design is now a very real thing. Not only do the computers perform the conventional calculations of the engineer, but interactive CRT's are in use for conceptual work in original design. When the original design takes the form of a model, digitizers are available which will translate that model into computer input. It is not uncommon to discover that product design engineering and manufacturing engineering have reunited. If they have not reunited, at least the line between them is becoming extremely diffused and fuzzy.

Elsewhere in the corporation, the computer is being used in market analysis, in inventory control and purchasing, in production planning, scheduling and follow-up in quality control, maintenance scheduling, cost estimating, accounting, payrolls, and all the other clerical functions. None of these functions are completely independent. Ninety percent of them are closely related and ten per cent of them are interdependent; therefore, a change in any one of these situations when taken note of by the computer, can and is transmitted to all of the others. With the use of a common data base for a company, all of these interrelationships are instantly achieved. Everyone who has a need-to-know is informed of any change.

This should not be referred to as an automated factory. It may not be automated at all. No factory is going to be more automatic than those functions which are pre-determinable and pre-recordable, but it is an organization whose management control is integrated and largely automated.

Some such factories already exist. The IBM plant at Endicott, New York, which produces the system 360 computer is an excellent example in the electronic field. The Sundstrand plant at Rockford, Illinois, which produces constant-speed drives for aircraft is a good example in the mechanical field; and there are others. These are the brave pioneers. It is probable that because they are the leaders, they will have made mistakes which will be corrected in the subsequent plants. At least they have made giant strides in these first attempts.

The Manager in the New Environment

Today, current, accurate data is pretty hard to come by unless you generate it yourself or see it generated. Our record systems will give us last week's data with great accuracy, all neatly tabulated and analyzed, but instant data is not so readily available. So, a lot of time is spent by managers running up and down the sidelines getting the current data for current decisions. When the manager does not have absolute information on which to base logical decisions, he has to use judgement, and many a manager is selected purely on his ability to exercise good judgment more than half of the time. That is to say, his intuition tells him what the facts probably are and the seat of his pants tells him what to do about it.

But under the new systems, management can have absolutely current data and have it processed any way it wishes. All the routine processing and routine decisions should be made for the manager and displayed for his approval. What does that leave the manager?

The manager has the true managerial functions left:

1. He does the long-range planning and formulation of objectives.

2. He formulates the decision rules that keeps the computer occupied.

3. He handles the nonroutine decisions for which there is no pre-programmed rule in the computer.

4. He makes subjective evaluations of the plant's accomplishment.

5. He attends to structuring the organization.

6. He attends to the staffing of the organization, the selection, training, and motivation of personnel.

7. He attends to the product and process innovation which keeps his company vital and viable.

8. Finally, he attends to external personal relations — relations with stockholders, vendors, customers, and the public.

That certainly is enough of a task for any manager and every bit of it is, at this writing, a function which must be carried out by a human. However, the intensity of managerial load placed upon a man can be a traumatic change from today's conditions.

Education

It seems clear that this new manager must be able to converse with the computer just as readily as students in their college days used the slide rule or the adding machine.

The new manager will also have to learn to cope with the Computer Department and its staff, who obviously would like to retain the unique pivotal position which they have achieved in the early days of the computer applications. The manager will have to learn to put the computer in the correct organizational status so that no one division of the company monopolizes its use or perverts its information to their personal advance-

ment. Finally, the manager will have to be prepared to assure the necessary security of access to the vast and vital store of information which is in
the computer. He must be able to converse not only with the computer
but with his peers in the other divisions of the company – R & D,
Marketing, Finance, and Manufacturing.

Conversing with people is a two-way task. Unless it is two way, it is not
a conversation. This means that the manager must be able to listen intelligently and to speak persuasively. He must be able to read intelligently and
write persuasively and he must give the other fellow a fair turn. The close
cooperation which is bound to exist between the manager and his peers
means that it is desirable that there be a compatability between them
based on common intellectual and cultural backgrounds.

Finally, the manager must maintain a high level of mutual respect
between himself and his peers based on his personal conduct as well as his
technical abilities. All of this presages a very different kind of education
for the manager. No longer may he be a specialist. By the same token, he
may not be a generalist, which is generally a "specialist promoted up-
stairs." Instead, he must be a multispecialist, and this is a very important
distinction.

The Personality Factors

The manager of the future must have an almost clinical understanding
of the sources of strain in a dynamic organization and a good understanding of what to do about it and how to do it. It's the author's experience
that the greatest sources of strain are change and innovation. Today's
technology brings an increasingly rapid succession of product changes and
innovations, an increasingly rapid succession of technological changes in
the factory, and the very managerial changes which have just been
mentioned. It is only human to resist change and the manager must not
only overcome this resistance in those who work for him, but overcome it
in himself.

The manager must participate in decision making, and must be capable
of assuming and carrying both the risk involved and the consequent
responsibility arising from his participation in decision making. Almost
every single one of the functions, which have been enumerated as being
left to the manager and as filling his day from end to end, are decision
making functions. If a manager is not capable of taking the information

available to him, formulating the question, and reaching a decision at a necessary and opportune time, then he will sooner or later fail and have to be removed from his managerial position.

Finally, the manager must be capable of surviving in a nonstable environment. There is very little that is stable in our world today to which we can tie and to which we can return as a firm base of operations. It takes a nimble manager to keep his balance in today's world and that is indeed a difficult situation for many people.

Summary

1980 will still see some plants indistinguishable from their counterparts of 1940. But, the new technologies are evolving rapidly and their adoption is progressing at an increasing pace. It is the intuitive awareness of a change in pace which has made automation a sensitive subject. Not only in the field of technology, but in the field of education and social relations.

The same applies to management and to managers. The evolution of new management techniques is slow — both in development and adoption. But the managerial techniques of automation must keep pace with the technology of automation and that is the task to which this symposium will direct its attention.

4

Delusions of Grandeur or the Elusive Fruits of Automation

Herbert W. Robinson

THIS PAPER IS SOMEWHAT PROVOCATIVE. It is intended to be. It is a plea for a return to realistic thinking and planning concerning the feasible rate of introduction of automation technology in the economy, and for a corresponding revision of widely-held expectations of what automation can actually accomplish for the human condition in the United States in the foreseeable future.

If we look back over the last 15 years, "automation" has been increasingly regarded as if it were a magic wand with which the United States is about to achieve instant abundance (i.e. within a few decades). Indeed, this view has become so fashionable that it has even led many to begin speculating on how we will be able to find work for everyone — or how we will use untold leisure time — when tremendously automated plants and service establishments enable only a handful of people to satisfy the material needs of tens of thousands. Some are already devoting mental energy to worrying about how society should look when we can produce five times our present income per head with only 10 percent of the labor force. If these delusions of grandeur were confined to only a handful of academicians they would not be so dangerous. However, politicians, labor leaders, and even the man in the street have taken it for granted that the breath-taking technological progress that has enabled man to land on the moon is readily transferable to production and that these kinds of developments are, therefore, just around the corner. Everyone seems anxious — many insistent — to lay hands immediately on the flood of easily-acquired income now in prospect and to start right now to spend it on higher standards of living and to see our governments initiate even more ambitious projects for the improvement of our society. Today, we are apparently so convinced that we will soon have all the quantity we need in the United States that we are beginning to turn our attention confidently to the so-called "quality" of living as a new and immediately attainable additional objective of society.

Experience of the 'Sixties

The experience of the 'Sixties demonstrates this prevailing attitude. It was taken for granted that America's bountiful natural resources, her superb "management," her dynamic free enterprise system and her rapidly developing scientific and industrial technology, would permit almost unlimited new major social projects, both Federal and State and Local, in the decade.

Defense preparedness predictably took greater and greater amounts of resources as an aggressively competitive Communist world grew faster than the U.S. in economic strength, and as modern warfare has become more and more technologically complex and therefore more capital-intensive. The defense burden has also been greatly exaggerated in recent years by the Viet Nam War. In current dollars, total outlays on national defense have risen from $46 million in 1960 to $81 billion in 1969 (of which Viet Nam took about $20 billion).

A succession of ambitious major social projects however, have also been introduced to the point where, in total, they have surpassed normal defense expenditures. The space program; the war on poverty; Federal natural resources, housing, health, education and welfare programs; all admirable in concept, have been piled one on the other by successive administrations. Federal outlays alone on these programs rose from $24 billion in 1960 to $64 billion in 1969 ($72 billion planned in 1970). And State and Local governments, whose purchases in total exceed those of the Federal government, more than doubled their expenditures in the decade. We seem to have proceeded on the assumption that the only limitations to economic progress are our imagination and ambition.

Let us now examine the actual history of the U.S. economy in the last five years of the decade of the "Soaring Sixties" in order to determine how far common impressions of rapidly rising productivity through automation, and the dawn of a new era of economic growth, are actually valid. The table in Figure 1 shows some key economic variables which describe the growth in output we have achieved, with what labor force it has been achieved, the productivity of the labor force, and the investment which was necessary to achieve the results. The overall picture is as sobering as a bucket of ice water.

In the five year period 1965-69, the GNP measured in 1958 dollars (a unit provided by the Department of Commerce which corrects for the effects of inflation) grew from $581 billion to $728 billion, an increase of

25 percent (at 1969 prices, the actual 1969 figure was $932 billion). Industrial production expanded 30 percent and agricultural production by nine percent. However, during the same period of time the U.S. population also grew rapidly and the civilian labor force expanded by 10 percent. Within the labor force, the number of persons employed in "service" establishments — trade, finance, services and government — grew 24 percent; in fact the growth in this category was 8.1 million people compared with a growth in the total labor force of 7.6 million so that productive people outside the "service" establishments actually fell by one-half million persons. The net result was that overall productivity, namely the output per head of the total labor force, actually increased only 12-1/2 percent in five years. Even worse, if we allow for the fact that in the same five-year period the unemployment rate fell from 5.2 percent to 3.5 percent, the productivity of the employed labor force increased only 10.7 percent. This amounts to a compound rate of increase in real productivity of only two percent a year! It should be stressed that, out of this output per head, we have had to provide the funds for all of the defense, space and social programs of our Federal, State and Local governments. Even at 1958 prices these have grown at the rapid rate of over six percent per

FIGURE 1 — Some Key Economic Variables

FIVE YEAR PERIOD 1964-69

	Units	1965	1969	Increase
OUTPUT				
Gross National Product	Billion 1958 dollars	581	728	25%
Industrial Production Index	1957-59 = 100	132	172	30%
Agricultural Production Index	1957-59 = 100	111	121	9%
LABOR FORCE				
Civilian Labor Force	Million	73.1	80.7	7.6 (10 %)
CLF in "Service" Establishments*	Million	33.4	41.5	8.1 (24 %)
Unemployment Rate	Percent	5.2	3.5	-1.7 %
PRODUCTIVITY				
GNP ÷ CLF	1958 dollars per head	$8,000	$9,000	12-1/2 %
Adjusted for Unemployment				10.7 %
INVESTMENT				
Private Non-Residential Fixed				
Investment **: Amount	Billion 1958 dollars	57.8	81.4	41 %
Percent of GNP	Percent	9.9	11.2	12 %

* Trade, Finance, Service, Government
** Structures plus Producers' Durable Equipment

annum (from $111.2 billion to $149.7 billion). As a result, personal consumption expenditures per head of the labor force have grown only just over two percent per annum and residential construction per head has actually fallen by over 12 percent. Is it any wonder then that the average wage-earner feels little, if any, better off than he did five years ago and that an air of economic frustration is widespread?

Even this small increase in productivity required heavy investment. In order to achieve an average two percent per annum increase in productivity it was necessary to invest about 10 percent of our total GNP in non-residential buildings, plant and equipment. In 1969 such investment was 11 percent of the GNP and amounted to $81 billion at 1958 prices (because of inflation, the actual 1969 figure, at 1969 prices, was 99.3 billion).

No Dramatic Increase

When we look at these cold figures it becomes obvious that, despite the improved technology of automation, we are not experiencing any very dramatic increase in overall output per head and, therefore, in available income per head. Average output per member of the labor force still is only $9,000 (in 1958 dollars) and achievement of increases in income per head through increased productivity are still extremely expensive. On the average we had to invest a total of about $900 per head per annum for every member of the labor force during the five years in order to obtain an average increase of about $200 per head per annum in productivity. Nevertheless, this was a net yield on investment of about 22 percent per annum. If these rates of investment and yield were to be maintained over the final three decades of this century we could expect another 80 percent increase in output per head, and in living standards, by the year 2000. However, this would still leave the output per member of the labor force at about $16,000 per annum (still measured in 1958 dollars), and, if the proportions in the labor force were to remain the same as in 1969, such a member of the labor force would have to support another one and a half people on the average. Certainly, even with continued full employment, we cannot see in these figures any sign of a millenium just around the corner that would support the kind of growth in social programs we have seen take place in the sixties.

The dangers of maintaining present illusions concerning possible major contributions of automation technology to the growth of productivity are very evident when we consider recent and current demands of labor for increases in salaries and wages and compare these with the actual increase in productivity achieved. Increases of 5 percent a year (average) are considered unambitious by today's standards. George Meany, President of the AFL-CIO, has recently made the carefully considered demand that in the year 1970 alone there should be an average increase in wages of 10 percent. He seems to be unaware that this would represent an increase in one year equal to the entire increase in real productivity per employed member of the labor force achieved over the past five years! It is no wonder then, that in such an atmosphere of wage increases, prices in those same five-years increased by 18 percent!

This rate of inflation is bound to continue until we realize that we must all face the facts of life; that overall increases in productivity require enormous investments that can only come out of presently available resources, and that the fruits of automation provide no open-sesame to abundance. To illustrate, to obtain Mr. Meany's 10 percent in one year would require an investment of the order of $250 billion (in 1958 dollars) and would use up about 30 percent of the present total GNP. Quite obviously, the major source of the funds to support this kind of investment would have to be found through a radical reduction in spending on goods and services used in everyday life. Allowing for that part of GNP already being used in investment and in government, the reduction in personal consumption would have to be something like one-third, obviously quite unacceptable to Mr. Meany since the very objective of his proposal is, presumably, an increase of 10 percent in the per capita consumption of the population.

While the technology of automation may hold out the promise of a gradual improvement in the above-mentioned 22 percent rate of return on investment over the years, the basic obstacle to human progress is the fact that to obtain an increase in the standard of living we must (a) replace existing capital equipment wearing out; (b) invest in comparable productive capacity per head for new entrants coming into the labor force as the population expands; and (c) invest across the whole labor force in improved technology, in order to secure the desired increase in productivity per head. And when we add up these three requirements we simply do not have enough investment capital being saved in the economy at current rates to be able to afford a rate of investment to sustain a markedly faster rate of growth. To illustrate with hypothetical orders of magnitude, if we assume that normal replacement of obsolete capital requires about three percent of the GNP, and that another two percent is required for growth in the labor force, then merely to double the rate of growth of output per head (and income per head) to a level of four percent a year compounded would necessitate increasing our present private non-residential investment by about 50 percent. And to finance this would mean an initial reduction of about eight percent in consumption expenditures on goods and services by the private sector of the economy, or, alternatively, a pause of about four years during which we enjoyed no increase in consumption whatever but channeled all our increased output per head into investment.

Constraints on the Fruits of Automation

We now have to ask ourselves how it is that, with all the apparent promise of mechanization and automation in manufacturing industry, transportation, and services, including the introduction in the last fifteen years of tens of thousands of computers in clerical and managerial activities, we have not been able, so far, to squeeze out a much greater rate of progress in our economy and society than we have.

Obviously, the point we have just brought out is fundamental. There is a definite limit, through voluntary savings, corporate internal investment and government investment out of taxes, to the amount that can be invested by the economy in any one year in additional capacity while still maintaining present living standards. Moreover, within this total, we have first to replace obsolete capacity and provide for the net increase in the labor force. We thus encounter a very definite limit to what can be invested annually in increased productivity, and especially in implementing automation technology. One answer to the anomaly of our slow growth, and to those who fear that a tremendous expansion of automation might soon put millions out of work, or create problems of boredom amidst abundance, is that there simply is not enough capital being saved by the community to afford any more than a very small increase in the degree of automation in the economy each year. Moreover, any radical increase in this rate in a free society such as ours is ruled out by the fact that it would require politically impossible austerity to achieve a rate of savings adequate to increase it substantially.

Massive Social Projects

Another basic obstacle to automation is the fact that, due to the above-mentioned popular delusions of grandeur concerning our potential to rapidly increase productivity in the economy, politicians and the public have developed an unbridled appetite for spending lavishly on new programs in the political and social areas. There is almost an open competition as to which political party can discover some new major crusade offering brave new worlds to the population. Each of these, as it comes on the scene, is — however attractive and laudable in its intent — another diversion of available funds from investment in the basic increase in productivity, an essential requirement if we are to finance these very programs themselves. To illustrate this point, consider three recent programs which have acquired almost universal support:

First, as a matter of basic national policy — from the finest of motives and for the best of reasons — we have, in effect, decided to increase rapidly the standard of living of the underprivileged and minority groups in our society. As a minimum this group represents of the order of 12 percent of the population. We are attempting, in the space of a few years, to achieve a quantum jump in the standard of living of the group by perhaps 50 percent. Even if we assume that the standard of living of these groups have been only one-half of that of the country generally, such an effort, by simple arithmetic, requires the provision of about an additional three percent of the whole GNP to their consumption annually. This would absorb almost all of two years normal increase in the whole nation's productivity and income per head, a cost which must be recognized. It is a sacrifice that must be made in order to achieve the social advance which we all desire, but the man in the street has little conception of its real extent.

Second, we seem to be developing a new philosophy under which the poverty-stricken old residential centers of our metropolitan communities are to remain as a solid mass, will be completely re-built where they stand, and must be provided with rapid mass transit to the suburbs where the work for their population now is. This is highly questionable from an economic point of view. Industrial development is certainly not going to take place in the center of our metropolitan areas under this concept — the land will be fully committed to housing — but will occur in the surrounding suburbs. Normally, housing for the labor force would tend to follow industrial development but what we are creating is a new, artificial, phenomenon — a central low-income dormitory. This will involve the daily transportation of huge numbers of people over large distances to remote places of work through mass transit systems built at enormous expense. The penalties are, first, the enormous economic cost of this unnecessary movement. Second, the fact that the inhabitants of the central city will have to spend perhaps up to two hours of their life every day in their journey to and from work. Third, the impairment of the normal function of the center of the metropolitan complex as a community, governmental, cultural, social, shopping and recreational center for the whole community. And finally, the income-stratification of society into large homogeneous globs instead of into the balanced communities having the economic and social intercourse and mobility that have been the foundation of American society in the past. We have here the irrational injection of political and socio-philosophical factors which are completely artificial and non-economic. They will distort the normal social and economic development of the community, which would, as in Europe, normally involve re-housing the innter-city population in the suburbs rather than in the inner-city. And the tremendous unnecessary expense can once again only come out of the rate of investment and hence impair our rate of growth of productivity and hence the rate of national economic progress.

Additionally, we are now embarking on even more ambitious projects of this nature: the provision of enhanced hospital and medical care on a tremendously increased scale overnight to the whole population; beautification programs; ultra-safety programs; and many other programs, which, though admirable in intent, assume an almost unlimited economic pocketbook. These involve additional diversion of investment funds to programs which will produce only minor corresponding increases in productivity. As such programs make inroads into the available funds for investment they still further inhibit the growth of productivity and national income. The present deep sense of frustration at the fact that, with the fastest technological progress in history, money wage increases seem to lead mainly to inflation and not to corresponding real income improvements may even be intensified by such programs. The net effect may be even more unrest and conflict and a deterioration rather than an improvement in the quality of life in America.

Uneconomic Activities

An additional constraint on automation is extremely fundamental and yet often overlooked. We cannot judge automation on a purely technical basis. Just because of the above-mentioned scarcity of investment funds — indeed as a reflection of it — we come up against the constraint of cost-effectiveness, or, as it used to be called, economic justification, of the innovation. Unfortunately, many of the most attractive and superficially most productive automation developments, while theoretically and technically feasible, prove, at any point of time, to be uneconomic. While sound and practical from a purely technical point of view, the costs of the process exceed what it is worthwhile spending to achieve the results obtained. Specific applications of automation which have been used in the space program for instance, where expense was almost no object, might well be a dismal economic failure in the industrial economy.

Here is a subtle mental block which lies in wait for all involved in the automation industry. The mere physical viability of an automation application does not assure its economic justification; it may well be that it cannot be introduced in the normal business environment on a profitable basis. It is essential, therefore, that we perfect methods of analysis to identify those applications which are truly economic at any particular time and those whose implementation must await a later stage of economic development.

Another major problem in the faster application of automation as a means of raising productivity rapidly, is the rather recent inexplicable strong trend toward service activities in the economy.* As the Figure 1 shows, whereas in 1964 only 46 percent of the labor force was in the service establishment, by 1969 over 51 percent were so engaged. Even this latter figure underestimates the true percent in"service" activities since our manpower figures for "establishments" do not include the self-employed and domestic workers (they account for a substantial part of the labor force not in establishments, which is some 7.8 million persons, or over 10 percent of the labor force).

It has been claimed that the industrial organization of the United States owes its high productivity to this very trend toward services, that it is a reflection of a higher-level technology which, while it demands more specialized professional and technical services, finally produces much superior ultimate economic efficiency. However, the lack of vigorous growth of overall productivity, already observed, hardly bears this out. One is tempted to speculate whether the service economy does not contain a substantial element of a "parasitic" economy! This growing percentage of service activities seems to act as a dead weight, a dampening factor, by offsetting to a considerable degree the impressive increases in productivity being achieved in the agricultural, extractive, manufacturing, construction, and transportation sectors of the economy. A relevant question here is whether the installation of automation equipment, while showing substantial direct returns from the investment on the production line, does

---

*i.e. Trade, Finance, Service and Government

not involve the supply of many ancillary services in the economy generally which pull down net productivity to levels normally experienced in the more mundane forms of industrial investment. One is also inclined to wonder whether a special tax on service activities would not be beneficial to the growth of productivity as well as rewarding to the Treasury at this state of our economic development.

One of the major difficulties we face is that automation has proven peculiarly inapplicable to the service area itself. which now takes over half our manpower. One has only to look at shops, stores, restaurants, hospitals, entertainment, beauty parlors, the vacation industry, recreational activities, etc., as well as the huge government sector, to see that the problem of automating services is an extremely difficult one. A basic reason for this is that, as our standard of living improves, we tend to demand personal services which can only be provided by individual human beings and are hard to provide mechanically by machines. The most promising area of application of automation in services, therefore, lies in automation aids to enable people themselves to give more and better personal services, and this is an area which has not adequately attracted the inventive genius in the automation industry thus far. One of the basic difficulties here is that the design of automation systems in the service area, because they must take account of the many personal idiosyncracies of the customers constituting the marketplace, is extremely complex and laborious, and the equipment itself extremely expensive.

Economic and Industrial Organization

Perhaps one of the major bottlenecks to the full exploitation of automation potential is the fact that at present it tends to be applied in relatively small economic units in the economy because at present the United States economy is simply not organized commercially and industrially to exploit the full benefits of automation. Automation is opening up the possibility of providing, in one single unit of capacity, enormous production potential to satisfy demand. Yet our present industrial and economic organization often fragments the supply, through the multiplicity of companies providing the product or service, into only small units of capacity which cannot exploit modern automation technology effectively. The systems approach to satisfying demand is inhibited by the scale of present operations. We face an era where considerable industrial reorganization may be required in order to provide units of a size which can both fully exploit automation technology and utilize the complete, comprehensive systems approach to the production and distribution of goods and services. There are endless examples of this problem. For instance, why should the householder send off twenty different checks to twenty different suppliers each month instead of one check? Why should an airport be organized on the basis of individual company counters and gates? Why should distribution of the numerous completely standard products be conducted so expensively through a tremendous network of individual retail outlets? In the next few decades it is essential that, if we are to apply the benefits of automation to production lines, transportation and distribution, and to the service functions in society, on a mass basis, industrial and commercial organizations be vastly rationalized through combinations and mergers, and through new and different approaches to the methods of doing business.

Available Competence

One reason for the slow pace of automation is the fact that today's automated equipment requires a very high level of competence from those who plan, program, manage, and run such equipment. The question arises whether, if we consider the normal distribution of the intelligence quotient in the whole population, we can, under present methods, find sufficient qualified people, especially sophisticated systems design engineers, to apply automation to more than a small portion of the total labor force. Unfortunately, present equipment is very demanding of advanced professional skills and, despite training programs, there has been a serious shortage of qualified personnel to operate even the small quantity of automation equipment which has been installed to date. Indeed, the lack of trainable personnel is probably one of the greatest bottlenecks which has held back the economy from harvesting the fruits of automation. (Parenthetically, it might be observed that there is a paucity of statistics with which to measure the extent of automation already introduced, and currently being introduced, into the economy; our investment statistics do not, as yet, distinguish automated as opposed to unautomated equipment.)

An important question is how far the obstacle to automation is truly inherent in the technology or lies with the automation industry itself. How far are automated machines and systems being designed by engineers and systems designers for engineers and systems designers themselves instead of for the personnel who are available to manage and operate them? It seems there is inadequate attention being paid in designing equipment to consciously reducing the level of intelligence or expertise required to operate the system, even if it does mean some increase in the cost of the equipment itself. What is needed is a deliberate effort to reduce the level of competence required at every stage, so that we can de-skill the job but upgrade the workers into positions which utilize automation equipment to the fullest extent possible. Indeed, we should be using automation principles themselves in our system design to substitute automation technology for human skill wherever possible in the operation of the system finally evolved.

The problems raised in meeting the exacting skill requirements of automation are, of course, exascerbated by the defense and space programs, which absorb enormous numbers of the limited number of available highly suitable scientific, engineering and professional personnel. When we consider the investment in high technology production capacity, and the type of manpower pre-empted in these programs we can only speculate how much civilian output could be produced if this capacity and manpower were converted to fully automated civilian mass production lines. It would be enormous. The cost of these programs to the nation's progress, therefore, is probably far greater than mere GNP figures would indicate. The potential growth of GNP which might be realized if this diversion of resources could be reduced is, therefore, substantial.

Conclusion

The preceding analysis has brought out the grave obstacles that are inhibiting us in applying automation technology to securing dramatic increases in productivity. If we were to be guided solely by the disappointing results of the last decade or two, despite an atmosphere in which automation was the "buzz-word" throughout industry and commerce, we may perhaps easily acquire a "gloom and doom" outlook regarding future prospects for automation and society. However, it would not be appropriate to leave the subject without a few words of encouragement, and to discern some rays of sunshine which illuminate and warm the future.

Assuming that the United States can honorably disengage itself from actual combat in Southeast Asia and elsewhere in the world, it seems likely that perhaps as much as $20 billion a year (in terms of 1958 prices about $14 billion a year) could be released from the defense program. This money, of course, is spoken for many times over by the ambitious social programs which abound on every side. However, if we consider that this would enable us today to add about 20 percent to our private industrial investment, this could well be the most productive area in which the money could be spent. Allowing for the fact that the resources employed in the defense program are so peculiarly well adpated to automation the net effect could well be as much as fifty percent increase in the rate of increase in productivity. By the end of the century we would then enjoy, not an 80 percent increase in output per head, but a 140 percent increase, a remarkable transformation.

The source of all expenditures is produced income; income cannot be spent before it is produced. The best way of obtaining the funds we need for the ambitious social programs now in the minds of our legislators and the public alike, is increased production through increased productivity. The fastest way to provide a better environment and a better society is through the expansion of productivity and income at the earliest possible moment. Technologically, we have tremendous potential in that there is virtually nothing that is physically impossible today; the only question usually is whether a particular innovation is economically justified. With present automation technology, computer technology, and communications technology, and the prospect of very substantial advances in all these areas, since they are still technologies in an early stage of development, the scope for employing capital productively in automation technology is enormous. It is, therefore, not inconceivable that present trends in the increase in income per head could in fact be doubled by a purposeful effort to attune the whole society to the concept of more investment in automation technology throughout every sector.

Thus, even though the conclusion of this paper must be that thus far we have suffered from delusions of grandeur and that the fruits of automation have so far proved elusive, we might yet, by setting more realistic goals, by making adequate allocations to investment, and by making deliberate efforts to harness effectively the power of automation, produce tremendous improvements in human welfare — economic, political and psychological — during the remainder of this century. However, we should be under no illusion that the achievement of such a transformation will demand wisdom, foresight, and determination from the best brains and leadership in our legislature, executive government, labor, management, industry and commerce. Above all, it will demand a sound knowledge, on the part of all concerned, of the ineluctable relationships which govern consumption, investment and productivity in our economy and a determination to see to it that the quantity of investment required to achieve substantially higher rates of increase in productivity is in fact forthcoming.

5

Automation Management in Education

Gordon B. Carson

AUTOMATION IN HIGHER EDUCATION has been confronted with both passive and active Luddism. The average professor sees in automation a considerable threat to his autonomy, and perhaps his security. Beyond this he has an ill-defined feeling that his academic freedoms are being abridged by the encroachments of automation. As a result, methods possible and equipment available based upon today's technology are frequently looked upon with disfavor and a lack of innovative spirit generally exists in the "groves of Academe."

Fortunately, there are exceptions, and certain individuals have made giant strides in the use of automation in higher education. In many instances, however, these have been individual efforts, laudable and purposeful, but not part of a plan of management improvement or of an overall objective of added quality in the higher educational system.

Automated Audio Library

Perhaps the first example of automation in higher education is the Dial Access Remote Station Listening Center. There are many in the country, but since the one at The Ohio State University was a pioneer installation, a few of the principles used will be delineated. The purpose of Dial Access Listening Centers on large campuses is to avoid the necessity for students to come to a central point. This eliminates crowded areas and the ensuing congestion. Such remote access provides ready availability to programs with lower time requirements for student study. The reasoning behind the system is based upon the fact that if a student wishes to use the eye as the window to the brain, he must carry the whole body to the point where the information can be seen, unless indeed a video readout is available. This, therefore, is the weakness of libraries, and a factor which makes the elimination of congestion in central libraries difficult, if not impossible.

Whenever the ear is used as the window to the brain, however, all one needs to do is gain access to an audio signal transformed into understandable common language. It is this technique which was used in the early decentralized listening centers on campuses. At Ohio State, there are 410 remote stations served by a central programming unit. Some 94 channels of information extending from Spanish and Russian to Music Appreciation are available to any student who has been given the dial code for that subject matter. The program is available continuously from 8 in the morning until 11 in the evening, 5 days a week; from 8 a.m. to 6 p.m. on Saturday; and from 1 to 11 p.m. on Sunday. It is also possible to have specific time programming where certain units of information are available during specific hours of the day. This automated device is a supplementary source of information not unlike the Library, except that it is the ear rather than the eye that is the window to the brain.

Professors have indicated that they can tell at once whether a student has been using the listening center to study for a language class, by his responses in class. The student who takes advantage of the automation is a better student.

One hundred ninety-eight stations are audio-passive, where only listening is possible. Two hundred twelve are audio-active, where it is possible to listen to the instructor, then repeat what the instructor has asked one to repeat, and hear it at the same volume as the instructor's enunciation. In this way, the spoken word can be learned much more rapidly, and errors ascertained and corrected.

The Automated Laboratory

Another type of automation used in higher education is that of the automated laboratory. There are several versions of these being used throughout the country, but I will use the Biological Sciences Laboratory in the University College at Ohio State as an example, simply because I am familiar with it.

In this laboratory, Professors Ben Meleca and Robert Menefee (now of the University of Maryland) had the idea that a student self-help laboratory would be an improvement over the scheduled laboratory system. To the educationist, this is called autodidactic learning. In the case of the Ohio State laboratory, there are nine modules, each served by an instructor. One module has a capacity of 26 carrels for students, the others are from 16 to 22 in size. This means that there is always an instructor available within a reasonable span of time to assist a student who needs help. Personalized instruction is enhanced rather than reduced by the system. During the Winter Quarter of 1969-70, 3700 students were served by this laboratory, which contains nine modules and has a total of 194 carrels or stations.

The student enters at the check-in area, picks up a tag for a carrel which is available in the module to which he has been assigned, goes to that carrel and places the tag on a hook outside the carrel. This indicates to the instructor that the space has been assigned. The student also acquires the material for the experiment next on his course agenda, and proceeds at his own rate to perform this experiment. The instruction for the experiment includes a taped lecture and slides which are played and shown on equipment which is in every carrel. Additionally, the carrel is equipped with the necessary microscopes, water supply, etc. If the student finds that he is not able to proceed, he simply flips the switch which turns on a light not unlike the hostess call-buttons in airplanes, and the instructor then proceeds to the carrel to assist him.

The advantages are many: first, a slow student can take longer to get the same amount of work done that a fast student has done rapidly. Additionally, many new avenues of inquiry have opened up because the student is able to proceed at his own pace; and if he wonders about something, he isn't running out of class time before he gets it understood. The autodidactic laboratory with automated equipment is indeed a step forward in higher education and does not abridge the academic freedoms some professors feel they might be losing. A further advantage is that the taped lecture material is geared to the experiment at hand. It is a case of "shooting with a rifle instead of a shotgun."

Furthermore, the best edited lecture material can be chosen for the sequence. The student is not subjected in one class to an expert lecturer and in another class to one who is less effective. Additionally, the best motion picture films or slides can be chosen from the wealth of material the country over, and the descriptive material on the tape can be provided by local lecturers so that it keys with the course work being given. In short, the program is better prepared, better presented, and better able to reach the student than the nonautomated programs. And he receives more personal attention.

Lecture Response System

Another advantage of automated systems is illustrated by the lecture response system now being used in University College at Ohio State. This is not a new system. It stems from the voting machines that have been in use in legislative assemblies around the country for a long time. In the case of the legislative voting equipment, the legislator pushes a key which indicates "yes," a key for "no" and sometimes a key for "abstain." An immediate tabulation is made as soon as the keys have been pushed so that the record of the vote can be seen on a board and taken immediately.

This rather old idea has been converted into a response system so that the student can key in his response as "A," "B," "C," or "D." The lecturer can pause, ask a question, tell the students what the key is and get an immediate response so that he has feed-back at once on how the program is being received. The percent of responses in each category is displayed immediately, electronically, and there is a readout on the lecturn so that the lecturer knows at once what the effectiveness is of a given technique. This should make it possible to correct techniques as a course unfolds and, further, to get immediate reactions from audiences without incurring the distortions of the passage of time.

Criticisms have been directed toward both the autodidactic laboratory and the lecture response systems on the basis that it is possible for the student to cheat. Indeed, it is. In higher education, however, it is high time we take the position that we will design the system for the student who wants to get an education. The cheater cheats only himself when he attempts such miscreance as a student.

Computer Assisted Instruction

Since Mr. Kenneth Powell of IBM used a model 650 in the Pittsburgh public school systems, it has been obvious that the computer, used directly by the student, could be a powerful teaching device. The efficacy of this teaching method depends almost entirely upon the ingenuity with which the computer is programmed, and the diligence and enthusiasm of the staff which directs and controls its use.

One example of the CAI system is the program at The Ohio State University. This system, financed through a grant from the Division of Health Manpower of The Public Health Service is currently under the direction of James V. Griesen and Robert Folk, M.D., (College of Medicine).

The IBM 1050 terminal which is used as a student station, is supported by the University's central IBM 50/75 computer.

The student uses a slide projector, which shows a section (for example) of human tissue on the backlighted viewscreen. The terminal, when the proper legend is typed in by the student, asks a question such as, "What organ or component of the body is this?"

The student responds by typing his answers. If the answer is right, the computer replies and states why it is the right answer. If the answer is wrong, the computer asks the student to try again, and gives a hint as to the makeup of the body areas depicted by the slide. The student keeps up the process until the answer is correct.

Meanwhile, the computer is recording in memory, a brief account of what transpired, and this will be reported to the professor who is the student's preceptor.

Course Planning and Scheduling

Education has been very slow to accept the possibilities of program planning for each student. Some universities, notably Purdue, have had partial registration programs on the computer and have been able to effect a certain degree of class and laboratory scheduling by automated methods. The fact is, however, most universities have failed dismally to come up with a viable program which pleases both faculty and students, alike.

Registration in almost all our universities is a traumatic experience for a student. A study made some years ago at Ohio State indicated that in the College of Arts and Sciences a student did not get his first choice of course or time of program 71 percent of the time. This, obviously, is not freedom of choice. The lack of getting first choice the first time certainly interferes with the effectiveness of the instructional program. More recently, "closed courses" are all too evident on campuses the country over and especially in large universities. There has been a tendency on the part of the faculty to schedule those courses which a given faculty load would permit, and to let the students shift for themselves beyond that point. If there ever was an attitude which justifies a student uprising, it is the cavalier fashion in which department chairmen, professors and other members of the academic staff treat student needs and demands for curricular choices on a reasonable time schedule.

It should be possible, considering the art we have available and the science which has been developed utilizing the computers for tracing programs and reporting thereon, to provide a student with a reasonable assurance that he or she will get the courses needed when they are needed. I do not want to leave the impression that in most cases this is just a matter of convenience. It is true that some students attempt to schedule courses between 10 and 1 and try to have the rest of the day free. But it is not that kind of latitude we are discussing in this paper. I am referring to courses which are prerequisite for other courses and which must be taken if the student is to qualify for a given degree program. In such an instance closed courses can force a student to go an extra quarter or two in order to complete the work. This capriciousness is certainly not proper in 1970.

The remedies are simple to state but difficult to implement. In the first place, it should be possible to program every student who enters a university for all four years of his undergraduate career, immediately after proper aptitude, interest, and achievement tests have been utilized to gain information on that student. Admittedly, these tests are statistically correct for a group, but not for each individual. They will, however, give results which are accurate in the aggregate so that if the general data are used in programming courses, the resultant accuracy should be sufficient for planning sections, staff, laboratories and hours at which classes and laboratories will be held.

Adversaries attack the idea of such programming on the basis that students frequently change their minds. They do. And they should. But with each ongoing quarter in which the student's curriculum is preprogrammed, the accuracy increases so that by the time the student is in his junior year, it should be possible to predict with astonishing reliability what courses, programs, laboratories and time schedules will be required in the university for the last two years of that student's career. Automated systems properly programmed should make it possible for a university to offer the courses when the student wants them, where they are wanted, and with only a rare case of closed courses confronting a student.

Additionally, such a program would force career choices at an earlier age and eliminate the ridiculous specter of students finishing an undergraduate career with no more idea of what they wish to do for a living than when they entered.

I should note for the record that such lack of career objectives may be regarded as an excellent thing by certain staff members of the halls of

Academe. It is my emphatic belief that a great deal of the unrest and unhappiness in this country today is caused by the late choice of a career on the part of many students, some of whom never do achieve career choices that are reasonable or attainable.

An automated system supported by a digital computer of large scale could provide every university with clear-cut data on which to plan curriculum, teaching schedules, student program, and capital improvements. We in universities are a long distance from this point now. The result is that we have wasted millions of dollars of both student fee money and state funds in our halting attempts to gage desirable needs and aims in the future.

Automated Libraries

Libraries have failed to keep up with modern needs. We attempt to measure our library effectiveness and quality by measuring the number of volumes the library has indexed. This is ridiculous. Library effectiveness should be measured by keeping a record of the demands that cannot be met by the library. I refer to demands for information addressed to the library for which there is not a timely response. The *reductio ad absurdum* in measuring library capability would be for a library to claim it had 4 million volumes, all of which happened to be the same book. The number of volumes on the shelf has nothing to do with library effectiveness. Library effectiveness has to be related to the speed with which information can be retrieved from that library and placed in the hands of him who needs to use it.

It is obvious that a random access system of data retrieval, coupled with a mechanical system for delivering books to a given place, offers much in improving library effectiveness. Such a system is to be tried in the new Medical Library at The Ohio State University. A Randtriever system of book delivery is on order and it is expected that a computerized random access index will provide the information needed by the budding young physician and by the faculty members who teach him. Hopefully, it will be possible to inquire on a keyboard about needed information and have a report back on what is in the library (in abstract form) so that a second indexing of those things really needed could go forward with speed and hopefully with precision.

None of the truly automated libraries is yet in effective service. So the project is a high-risk experiment, but Dean Richard L. Meiling of the OSU

College of Medicine is hopeful that the new library will revolutionize university libraries and provide a student with a greater fund of information than he has ever been able to call upon in previous years. The problem will probably be one of reducing data to a Reader's Digest type of abstract without loss of meaning. This should be possible since so much of academic writing seems to be measured by the number of words it contains rather than the amount of information it transfers.

Areas for the Fruitful Use of Automation

We could revise the lecture method of teaching completely. For example, if a course is dealing with the causes of World War II, the professor now gives the class his interpretation of what happened. It would be better to have a video-audio series based upon Neville Chamberlain's utterances, Winston Churchill's orations, the diatribes of Hitler and Mussolini, and the recorded statements of Stalin and Tojo (with accurate synchronized translation) as the basic text material. Then the student can view and listen, review and re-listen as his needs dictate. Interrogation sessions would provide the necessary stimulus for keeping up. And many new vistas of learning would thus be opened. Hopefully, a new generation could make progress beyond that now possible.

Summary

There are three essential areas in which automation can be exceptionally helpful in higher education. These are as follows: (1) Improved teaching techniques including autodidactic learning systems; (2) registration, fee payment and curriculum planning (the housekeeping of higher education); (3) libraries — information retrieval.

These obviously are not the only areas in which automation can be helpful in higher education but if these areas are automated effectively, higher education will be able to transmit more knowledge in a given length of time, more effectively, than it ever has been able to cover before. More importantly, higher education will be able to teach more people how to think accurately, and to evaluate the premises on which reason is to be built. The old ideas of the time required to matriculate for various degrees will have to be revised. And, finally, the cost of higher education can either be reduced, or its upward progress can be arrested. All of these things will be markedly helpful as the oncoming generation of students looks to us for improved systems of higher education.

6

Management of
Data Automation

Joseph B. Warren

IN JUNE OF 1966 President Johnson signed a memorandum to the Heads of All Federal Departments and Agencies calling for improved management of automation in the Government. The President pointed out that:

"The electronic computer is having a greater impact on what the Government does and how it does it than any other product of modern technology."

Few will take issue with this statement. The Federal Government is the largest single user of automatic data processing (ADP) equipment. The inventory has grown to well over four thousand systems and annual cost now exceeds $1.9 billion. It is appropriate to note that the Department of Defense accounts for fully two thirds of the inventory and costs. Observations in this paper will be primarily concerned with experience in the Department of Defense where automated systems have flourished for the past 15 years.

Management Problems Created

The management problems created by the development of systems which prompted the President's memorandum in 1966 are still with us in 1970 and I am not sure we have made a great deal of progress toward achieving the rather simple objectives set forth in that memorandum, which were to: "... provide better service to the public; ... improve agency performance; ... reduce costs."

The management of automatic data processing in the Government has been the subject of legislation, Congressional investigations, Presidential messages, and a plethora of directives and regulations. The problems being attacked, however, remain relatively unchanged and have become so chronic they may be stated as axioms.

1. Most systems are underdesigned. That is, by the time equipment has

been acquired, programs written and data bases created, the equipment will not be capable of processing all data as frequently or as fast as required.

2. The workload at a given computer installation will expand to absorb all the time and resources available. This "Parkinson Law" of computers limits the ability of the installation to quickly respond to high priority work without disruption to scheduled work.

3. Planned costs of updating and expanding systems will be underestimated. The costs of reprogramming and retraining of personnel will probably equal or exceed system design and hardware costs.

In reviewing the past fifteen years, a period during which automation has grown from initially zero to an annual cost of about $1.2 billion, it is not clear that we have in fact enriched our knowledge of how to manage automation through 15 years of cumulative experience, rather it seems that we have just repeated one year's experience 15 times.

We find some comfort in the fact that the cost of computers is stabilizing at about 1.3-1.5% of the total Defense budget. As we shall discuss, every functional area in the Department, logistics, personnel, research and development, financial control, etc., has significant projects in operation or in development which depend on automation, and every aspect of management has felt the impact of this pervasiveness.

Rethinking of Major Tenets

We've seen that the growing use of computer-based systems during the most recent few years has caused a rethinking of some major tenets of management. This will, in turn, cause us to rethink some of our objectives for computer use and may alter the way we manage computers themselves.

It is important to note that — despite differences in size or mission — the problems we face in the Department of Defense are not unlike those faced in industry or education. In an intensive survey of the practices and problems in managing computers of a group of large industry and university computer users we found many common problems and unresolved issues. For example, problems existed in the areas of third-party leasing; emulation; centralization of the computer facility, of the systems design activity, and of the data system itself; the use of the computer and the data that it generates. Therefore, in view of the commonality of problems,

I am very confident that our experience in the DoD is relevant outside the Department.

I would like to recount a few statistics we have gleaned from our management information systems for computers in the Government, the Automatic Data Processing Equipment Inventory.

Total costs for ADP in fiscal year 1969 were reported to be about $1.2 billion, with the projected increase for 1970 over 1969 to be about 14 percent. This increase is roughly the same as the increase for last year. The Defense Department represents 63 percent of the number of computers in the Federal Government, and this statistic excludes a large number of special-purpose computers. Salaries for personnel in ADP in the Department of Defense came to $641 million in 1968, which was over twice the rental costs of $261 million, in the same year. This represented an aggregate use of almost 82,000 man-years of effort in ADP. Nearly 2900 different computer systems were reported. Projections for 1970 indicated accelerated growth in requirements for manpower although not in the numbers of computers.

How Are Computers Used?

It is interesting to see how computers are now being used in the DoD, and thereby to see where they are having an impact. The largest group of computers devoted to a single function is in logistics, for the management and control of the supply, transportation, and maintenance functions throughout the Department. This accounts for over 26 percent of the DoD computers. Next, we see that 25 percent of the computers are devoted to multifunctional applications at the base, camp, command and headquarters levels. After that, we see 18 percent devoted to Research and Development functions, 12 percent to pay, personnel, or accounting and finance functions, 7 percent to communications functions, and the remainder to weather, intelligence, command and control, and other functions. We see, then, that all the functional areas are covered and automation is used for almost every conceivable purpose. A complete breakout by function is shown in Figure 1. There is no end in sight for continued expansion of the impact of computers and computer-based data systems.

This diversity is not unlike that seen in industry. We often take as a model the rapid advances being made by industry in their application of such techniques as time-sharing, computer aided instruction, real-time inventory control, and computer-based decision-making.

I would like to review some experience in the evolution of computer-based data systems. By the very size of the DoD, such a functional area as logistics requires large and extensive data systems. On any particular base or control point, the system, while big and expensive, is not necessarily overwhelmingly complex. Taken together, however, the wide variety of individual data systems, from those monitoring the inventory on board ship or at a distant base to the very large systems tracking and managing millions of items on a world-wide basis, forms an overall data system of very great complexity.

As data systems are developed in more and more functional areas, and as each data system itself becomes larger and more pervasive, we have

FIGURE 1 — ADP Distribution as of Dec. 31, 1969

MAJOR FUNCTION OR USE	NUMBER OF COMPUTERS	% OF TOTAL	MONTHLY[1] RENTAL (000)	5 OF TOTAL
1. Base, Camp, and Station Management (Multi-functional)	624	20.7	4,764	12.0
2. Command and Headquarters Management (Multi-functional including system design centers)	140	4.7	2,630	6.6
3. Logistics a. Supply				
(1) Base Level	190	6.3	1,663	4.2
(2) Depot Level	282	9.3	3,741	9.5
(3) Inventory Control Point Level	216	7.2	4,660	11.9
(4) Cataloging and related logistic services	7	.2	299	.7
b. Transportation	17	.5	147	.4
c. Maintenance	87	2.9	122	.3
4. Military Pay	146	4.8	399	1.0
5. Military Personnel Management	76	2.5	661	4.2
6. Accounting and Finance	34	1.1	322	.8
7. Communications	216	7.2	1,531	3.9
8. Weather	29	.9	887	2.2
9. Intelligence	122	4.1	2,642	6.7
10. Command and Control	103	3.4	2,694	6.8
11. R and D	533	17.7	10,069	25.5
12. Contract Administrative Services	23	.8	193	.5
13. Miscellaneous	144	4.7	1,101	2.8
TOTAL	2989		39,529	

[1] Use equivalent monthly rental for purchased computers.

found that computer-based data systems, by their very nature, require a certain degree of standardization and centralized management. The development of computer-based logistics systems has followed an evolutionary process from single applications at individual installations to command and Service-wide applications. Continued development of these systems is dependent upon the success of efforts to develop uniform data handling formats — which will allow compatibility of separate systems — and a much higher degree of coordination and control of computer-based data systems. We have seen the responsibility for this coordination and control elevated gradually from the installation level up through major command and finally to the Service headquarters level.

Wider Range of Functions

A much wider range of functions are being included in automated data systems, in part to meet the information requirements of high levels of management. This pattern — an elevation of responsibility for management of a function made possible, and necessary, by the elevation of responsibility for development, coordination, and control of the data systems — will be seen as well in the other functional areas that were discussed earlier as those functions expand their use of computer-based data systems. This high level management involvement is needed to insure that the data systems encompass all functions having common applications, and to insure that they will be compatible with other related systems. We can see a significant example of this evolution of development approach if we look at the history of systems for logistics management in the Department of Defense. The numbers involved are impressive: 700 computers — the largest single application of ADPE in Defense — are being utilized in the management of a $42 billion inventory, which includes more than 4 million stock items.

The first generation of computers was essentially carrying out applications which had been converted from large punched card operations. With the introduction of second generation computers, and as experienced personnel became available to exploit them, integrated data systems, encompassing major portions of the logistics program were developed, first at the individual installations level and then at the command level. Between 1960 and 1964, each of the Services and the Defense Supply Agency undertook major intra-Service standardization of supply systems. We are now in process of developing Service-wide systems for other functional areas and phasing out first and second generation systems.

The development of these large scale systems dictated new approaches to both logistics management and computer systems development. These systems also necessitated the establishment of headquarters level organizational groups to control and coordinate planning and development of computer-based systems. Each of the Services is now developing, modifying, refining, or expanding every level of operation.

Service-Wide Approach

The advantages cited by the Services in adopting a Service-wide approach to the design and development of standardized systems are: more effective management control; increased logistics responsiveness; better utilization of the critical resources of automatic data processing systems analysts and computer programmers; significant economies from reduced inventories, reallocation of manpower, and reduced needs for retraining.

An important point here is that practical, and if you will, political considerations prevent us from immediately taking the next logical step, that of standardization on defense-wide systems for similar functions across the various Services. Irrespective of arguments that DoD-wide systems would yield even more of the advantages cited above, there is enough for us to do in data systems design for the individual Services and Agencies in the development of effective systems to keep us usefully occupied for the next few years.

With this view of systems design evolution as background, consider for a moment the experience with some of the large automated systems in the

FIGURE 2 – History of Large Automated Systems

TYPE	ADP	COST (Millions of Dollars) SYSTEM DEVELOPMENT	YEARS DEVELOPMENT TIME*	NUMBER OF ACTIVITIES SUPPORTED
Inventory Control	71	32	5.1	10
Field Activity Support	62	17	2.6	146
Inventory Control	36	12	4.3	6
Inventory Control	27	4	3.5	12
Depot Operations	25	4	4.4	10
Field Activity Support	10	10	5.1	6

*Measured from project approval to initial implementation

Department of Defense. As can be seen from the data in Figure 2, these are large-scale, long-range projects.

It is immediately apparent that the development of an automated system requires a long range commitment of resources on a large scale. Delays and cost increases have become so customary that they are accepted as a natural occurrence.

There have been innumerable studies, and a vast amount of research, most of it in the nature of post mortems, seeking to find the key to success in the management of automation. The conclusions of these studies and research reports are as alike as peas in a pod. They invariably conclude that success can be assured only through direct top management involvement. The recommendations of these reports closely parallel those of Peter Drucker's "The Practice of Management." In substance these reports usually conclude that top management, particularly the chief executive, should do his job. The recommendations are usually in the form of a handy list of his duties. They are easily recognizable and familiar to Drucker readers: Set objectives; organize activity; motivate and communicate; measure performance; develop people.

These recommendations are so sound and obvious that they cannot be faulted. They have not provided any real solution to the problems in management of automation because for one thing they haven't really been followed and second, and more important, most managers seem to have adopted the concept that automation is a relatively new technology and demands new management concepts. The old principals of assigning personal responsibility and holding individuals accountable for their performance seem to have been abandoned. Computer technology was such a boon in the early years that no matter how badly systems were managed they had a positive payoff. It has been customary to accept failure and mismanagement as part of the new technology. This is now taking its toll. We should reflect on some recent comments in a study by a well-known consulting company, "In terms of economic payoff on new applications . . . the computer revolution in United States business . . . is rapidly losing momentum." A widely quoted article in *Fortune* by Tom Alexander discusses the failure of the promises of computer-based management systems to materialize.

Criticism of Management

Automated systems in the Defense Department have come under fire from Congress in recent years. The House of Representatives Committee on Defense Appropriations has been very critical of the management of ADP and expressed their disenchantment with automation by cutting about $100 million out of the Defense Department request for funds in fiscal year 1970 for ADP. The key to the committee's concern was unmistakably clear in the statement by one of the members, "Let us get to the heart of the committee's concern — is it worth the money you are asking for?"

Look at airline reservation systems: the SABRE system of American Airlines notwithstanding, many of the efforts to date have been failures. I refer to the recent cancellations by United and TWA of their contracts with UNIVAC and Burroughs, respectively. These airlines apparently did not feel that the computer systems proposed would have been used effectively, or that they were too costly, or that they were not responsive to the airlines' needs. It was most likely a combination of all three. At any rate, disenchantment was evident in the announcements of the cancellations.

Experience in the Defense environment is not strikingly different. The Semi-Automatic Ground Environment (SAGE) system went through a number of well-publicized and costly changes. Defense is currently agonizing over the scope, management, and design of a system for World-Wide Military Command and Control, known as WWMCCS. The problems with SAGE involved the determination of the appropriate level of interaction for the human operators more than they did the inadequacies of the hardware. The problems associated with WWMCCS are entirely management. Again, the problems are those of setting goals, clearly defining objectives, and managing resources. The problem is not one of hardware or technology.

Technology Not the Constraint

The capability of hardware and technology have far outstripped our expectations but the results we have achieved have fallen far short of our goals. It is most timely that we should focus on the management aspects of automation. We do not have technology problems; we have people problems.

During the first decade of DoD's experience with the management of computers we emphasized the management of hardware — its design, acquisition, operation, and maintenance — rather than the management of the people who carry out these functions. We seem to have placed technical experts in a privileged position where computer hardware is blamed for failures or errors rather than the people who wrote and implemented error-ridden, failure-prone data systems. This seems to be true for large as well as small computer-based data systems.

In the majority of cases, however, failure can be traced to human failures — failure to design well, failure to implement carefully, and failure to assure reliable computer operation. However, we are more inclined to tear out the computer than we are to fire the programmer.

I would like to offer the following speculation: As computer applications come to have a more direct impact on the activities of every organization, management attention must be focused on the people involved in computer systems — as designers, programmers, users, and recipients of computer-provided services — or there will arise a misplaced reaction against the continued application of computers to the solution of problems. We can see an example of this in an application as prosaic as the servicing of department store charge accounts: So long as the department store wrote, "Do not fold, spindle, or mutilate" on correspondence with its customers, the customers felt "used" by an impersonal system. They associated billing problems and errors with the computer. Lately, by designing billing systems with the customer and her disinclination to be forced into a rigid structure in mind, systems designers have made them more palatable and hence more successful.

Automation Scapegoat for Human Errors

We have fallen into the habit of using automated systems as the scapegoat for human error and failure.

A logistic manager of a key operation in the Pacific complained that vast quantities of equipment and material were building up at his control point and he was losing the capability to control the inventory. His problem — as he described it — was that the computer available wasn't capable of processing data fast enough and the solution was simply to get a larger computer.

The Commander of a supply center recently converted his system from a second generation computer to a third generation computer. The entire system had been redesigned, programs rewritten and extensive testing conducted over a three-year period. As soon as the new system was put into operation it began to flounder and his mission performance was jeopardized. Again the blame and responsibility were not attributed to human failure but to the size and capability of hardware. The proposed solution was the same — a bigger and faster machine.

A celebrated case of "Computer error" is that of E.A. Fitzgerald who had his job tenure withdrawn while testifying before Congress on cost overruns on the C-5A. Mr. Fitzgerald at the time was an Air Force employee in the Office of the Secretary of the Air Force. He had fallen into disfavor for his outspoken criticism of Air Force procurement practices. The question of retribution against Mr. Fitzgerald was raised during the committee hearings and Air Force witnesses gave assurance that no action against Mr. Fitzgerald was planned. When the tenure of office was made and withdrawn the explanation given was the the the offer was simply a "computer error." It is true that the offer of tenure was not appropriate but the culprit was an unnamed and unidentified machine rather than any flesh and blood human being.

I am sure that most of us have been "folded, bent or spindled" by computers at one time or another and can appreciate the reaction at one of the largest state universities when half the freshman class received failing grades due to a "computer mistake." This was at a time when satisfactory grades for the male students were essential to avoid being drafted.

New Direction Required

There is ample evidence at hand to convince anyone that we must take a new direction in the management of large automated projects. The use of computers to solve data processing problems no longer falls under the heading of research and technology. Herein lies a principal reason for the difficulties that systems encounter in their formative stages. System administrators have simply become inured to the estimates, delays and difficulties that characterize research projects. They have not insisted on visible progress and measurement of well established goals. Project managers are measured more by the complexity of their difficulties than by the success of their projects.

In the Department of Defense we are faced with the necessity for a more quantitative approach to the management of ADP systems development. One of the first considerations is the documentation of a well thought out set of measurable objectives which the system will be expected to meet. Along with this should be a delineation of exactly how these objectives will be measured and met. While this virtually does away with such objectives as "better information," it does substitute targets to be aimed for. The next consideration will be to identify all resources which will be assigned to this discrete project. These resources take the form of such things as salaries, man-hours, contracts and computer time. Once we have put a bound on the project and the assigned resources, the next step is to perform a classical economic analysis to determine the cost-effectiveness of that which is being proposed. The full cost and the attendant benefits should be revealed. If the venture is in fact cost-effective, there is little question as to approval to go forward. If the venture is not cost-effective, the approving authority should have the cost of the approval decision known to him, and make his decision in full knowledge of this, and have this decision documented. This does not mean that every decision must be cost-effective, but it does mean that decisions in this area must be made in an environment where all known facts that bear on the case are revealed.

The next consideration is the visibility of the progress being made. It is important that both advances and adversities be given high visibility and that timely action be taken to correct any deficiencies. We are currently developing a procedure whereby the ADP system development administrator will identify key milestones, forecast his resource utilization to these milestones and then measure himself against the forecast when the milestone is actually achieved. He will forecast again at each milestone, for some number of milestones in the future. However, he will be measured and judged explicitly on the forecast from the present to the next succeeding milestone. In other words, at each milestone he is making a firm commitment to the next milestone, and concurrently giving his best estimate of the milestones beyond that. There is a threshold of variance of actual from forecast (time and money) which, if violated, will require an in-depth system review. Otherwise, the system proceeds as planned. In conjunction with this tracking of the system, an updating of the economic analysis will be required at each milestone.

Summary

Management of automated systems is a constraint to achieving the potential of computers.

Management problems in the development and implementation of automated systems are essentially the same as in other fields.

People must be directed, motivated and controlled if we are to achieve system objectives. This means that personal responsibility for performance must be demanded. Technology is not lagging and should not be an excuse for human failure or substandard performance.

7

The Planning Imperative

Melvyn R. Copen

IN RECENT YEARS, the need for more effective methods of planning for automation has become urgent. Although automation has been the key to most of the material benefits of industrial society, it has also sired or nurtured many current social problems, the magnitude of which seems to be increasing exponentially. The situation is made even more critical by a growing sense of public frustration and impatience. Unless we learn how better to use the technology we have — to predict its impact in the broadest sense, and to insure that the net effect is in accord with society's goals and objectives — we may be facing serious trouble.

The term "automation" is used here in a very broad sense — the application of technology to reduce the human effort required to achieve a given objective. It is a process, and we are concerned with planning for that process. The particular technology employed is irrelevant.

In the past, automation planning tended to focus on specific industrial problems such as moving materials between work stations in a more efficient manner. Plans were often framed primarily in terms of economic (e.g. cost) or physical (e.g. space) objectives. The focus was on the technology, with only grudging attention attention directed toward the most obvious elements in the technological-human interface. Typically, the scope of planning efforts was confined to the effects on the immediate department of departments concerned. Only later, as we began to develop the concepts of systems theory, did suboptimization rear its head. More recently, automation planning has begun to encompass the total enterprise, with departments viewed primarily as subsystems of the whole.

It is becoming increasingly evident that the cumulative effect of actions taken in departments and companies extends beyond corporate boundaries, reaching our communities, nations, and even our globe. Because we did not recognize the wider relationships, many past decisions have tended to suboptimize, at the expense of the higher-level systems. The pressures applied by population growth, better communications facilities, more rapid means of transportation, and higher educational levels have begun to awaken us to the need for more comprehensive approaches to planning. We are beginning to realize that we operate, in both our industrial and our private lives, in closer quarters than distance or density alone seems to imply. We are starting to view our world in terms of systems and subsystems, linked not only by telephone lines and highways, but also by rising expectations, and concepts of social justice. We must find better ways to reflect and incorporate these linkages in our planning processes.

The environment in which we live is a very complex system comprised of numerous elements, a few clearly defined, most somewhat nebulous, and probably many still to be identified. Consequently, it seems more efficient to treat the macro level by examining some of the key planning issues and problems in the smaller and simpler subsystems of the micro level (i.e., the individual enterprise) and then extrapolate to the higher level. Although the nature of the problems may change as we make this shift, the planning process should remain relatively stable.

Planning at the Micro Level

Within companies, automation planning can be divided into three categories according to breadth of analysis. The first and narrowest can be called "impulse automation." It often results when a manager of group of executives becomes enamored with a particular concept or device per se. Little or no advance planning is involved. "Situational planning" requires broader perspectives. It is frequently found when management either sets out to solve a particular problem by eliminating the visible symptoms or attempts to find applications for a new automation concept or device. "Comprehensive planning" is the most complex of the three. It begins with corporate goals and objectives and involves both a blueprint for future action and an analysis of particular alternatives in the light of their contribution to these goals and objectives.

Impulse Automation

"It must have been one helluva convention. The day after Mr. Williams[1] returned we were told to expect delivery in about six months of a process

---

[1] The name is disguised.

control computer for plant number five. Responsibility for installation and operation was to be shared jointly by the production manager (for obvious reasons) and the comptroller (because he had been looking after a computerized payroll and data processing system and was the only one in the company with any computer experience). It came as a bolt out of the blue, since we had never even discussed the possibility before."

This comment was made by an executive about four years after the process control computer had been installed in plant number five and about one and a half years after it had been removed. The three years of effort which had gone into this installation were considered to be a total loss, and had placed severe strains on the resources and morale of the firm.

A company which had outgrown the hardware it was using for a manufacturing information system changed companies when it installed a larger computer and, consequently, had to redesign its entire system − a task which required almost two years and resulted in sharply reduced productivity, a number of lost customers, many resignations, and several firings. An after-the-fact review indicated that very little effort would have been required (at an equivalent purchase price) if the company had purchased a bigger machine from the same vendor. The decision was made by one man − the controller − the company's only top level executive with computer experience. At a computer convention, he had approached the original vendor's regional manager who, failing to recognize the controller, had politely brushed him off.

These examples, severe in terms of their consequences, are typical of the lack of systematic planning for such matters found in many organizations. Neither of these firms would have allowed one man to make decisions relating to the introduction of a new product line, nor would they have approached financial resource allocation problems without comprehensive budgetary planning. But automation was not seen in the same terms.

Often, managements tend to respond to fads − to be the first on the block to obtain a certain computer or N/C machine tool or aircraft. The assumption is made that increased technology is intrinsically good and that this is a universally accepted value. It is just not so, and overlooking the fears and insecurities of individuals who will be affected by the change often creates unnecessary and major difficulties.

Impulse automation presents two serious problems. First, substantial effort is often channeled into justifying the decision, at the expense of an objective analysis of the situation. Second, the negative impact on other elements of the system (e.g. cost, morale, and other linked processes) can be severe, especially if no groundwork is laid to pave the way.

Situational Planning

Situational Planning involves both analysis and evaluation: a firm is faced with a problem and attempts to solve it; or a manager learns of a new advancement in automation and examines operations to see where the device or concept might best be utilized. Such planning tends, however, to be fractionated. Usually, the primary relationship to corporate goals is an attempt to justify any decision on the basis of contribution to profit. Each issue is treated separately, and when the problem comes in the form of a crisis, situational planning can easily turn into impulsive action.

Situational planning gives rise to at least four major problems. First, it tends to confine inputs to the people and functions directly concerned, often eliminating useful information sources which could be tapped if broader participation was involved. Creative suggestions are lost, and often companies find themselves re-inventing their own wheels.

> A division of one major U.S. company spent months in a not too successful attempt to design a computerized production control system before it learned, by chance, that another division, manufacturing a completely unrelated product line, but using processes and facing customer demand patterns which were similar, had developed an almost identical system which had been operating successfully for several years.

A second problem is that by involving only those managers whose functions appear to be directly affected, many consequences of a particular decision may be overlooked. We are only beginning to develop skills in identifying the complex relationships which link elements which, previously, may have seemed unrelated. Broader participation in the planning process will not eliminate, but it may tend to reduce the number of unforeseen consequences.

> The production manager, a purchasing agent, a production planner, and a marketing manager made the decision to install numerically controlled machine tools in one company. The decision was based on economic calculations which indicated that the machining capabilities of the N/C equipment would lower production costs to a point which would enable the company to submit a low bid on a series of very profitable defense contracts. After installation, it was discovered that the major contributions to lower costs resulted not from reduced tooling costs. On the other hand, the equipment's sensitivity to temperature changes necessitated unforeseen construction expenses; the company had to reorganize its maintenance functions and hire an electronics specialist, which created both a union jurisdictional dispute and a wage level dispute; and, much to the surprise of management, the operators of the new tools demanded a substantial pay raise.
>
> Another firm discovered that it virtually had to enter the business of instru-

ment design and manufacture to make its computerized process control installation work.

A third problem in situational planning results from a tendency to de-emphasize the human element. The technologies and the economics receive most of the attention, and only cursory thought is devoted to the desires and attitudes of operators and users. Although the ultimate purpose of every management action is, in some manner, to alter human life, decisions are often made as if the entire system consisted of machines serving machines.

In one company, top management was surprised by its foremen's negative reactions to an overhead conveyor which was installed to store and transport work in process. The device contained a console which indicated the total number of items stored in the system and their particular locations, and it allowed the foreman to deliver any item to any work station by the push of a button. However, the foreman had become accustomed to scheduling work on the basis of the size of the piles on the floor and had also used these visual cues as measures of individual worker efficiency. They resented this new process which had been introduced after a short briefing session and which now deprived them of something they felt to be very important.

Another example of the tendency to de-emphasize the human element can be found in the computerized accounting and billing systems employed by many large "consumer-oriented" companies. Although these billing systems are usually the firms' primary interface with their human users, many are not designed to respond effectively to human communication.

One large credit company "personalizes" its service by assigning to each card holder a "personal representative" who may be contacted if a problem arises. However, unless the card holder writes in FORTRAN or COBOL, he is not likely to get a response.

Finally, situational planning is often wasteful because it tends to result in a patchwork approach to systems design, much akin to a trial and error approach at constructing a crossword puzzle. The first words come easy, but as the puzzle starts to fill out, the linkages become more restrictive, and the task may require frequent chains of changes in the work which has preceded.

Over a period of years, the data processing group of one educational institution had developed more than 380 separate programs and numerous data files in response to requests from academic units for specific kinds of student information. Finally, the "system" became so bogged down that the university was forced to build an integrated academic information system. It had to start from scratch. The new system which was developed used a single data base and a handful of inter-linked programs. It provided all of the functions previously performed plus many more, with quicker response time, and at a considerable reduction in maintenance and operating cost.

Because situational planning usually occurs in response to particular operating problems, it is often confined to middle management levels. Frequently, top management's only involvement is to approve or disapprove the specific capital investment requests which ensue. Yet, unless the goals and objectives which have been formed at top levels have been clearly communicated throughout the organization, there is strong likelihood that such decisions will tend to be sub-optimizing.

Comprehensive Planning

Comprehensive Planning is not the panacea for all of management's automation problems. However, it does increase the probability that actions will contribute to the long range goals of the enterprise, and it often identifies and forestalls many of the problems which would otherwise result.

A few years ago, a large machine tool manufacturer embarked on a diversification and expansion program which it hoped would achieve a modest but steady sales growth rate, would maintain or slightly reduce manufacturing costs, and would reduce some of the sharp fluctuations in production levels which had been experienced in the past. Management, believing that better information was the key, both to the selection of products for diversification and to cost control, began to think about an integrated, computer-based information system encompassing the accounting, financial, marketing, and production functions.

First, it formed a project task force consisting of representatives from each of the functional areas, from its unions, and from corporate headquarters. Two experienced systems analysts were hired and placed on the team, and each of five potential vendors was invited to send a representative. The task force reported directly to corporate headquarters.

The project was divided into four phases. The first required more than four months for completion and focused on defining meaningful systems goals (within the broad framework of company objectives), establishing standards to measure contribution to goal achievement, and identifying sources and uses of information.

In the second phase, sub-committees explored various alternative system configurations, identified the specific functions and individuals which would be affected by the introduction of such a system, and, finally, began to evaluate vendor proposals. During this phase, specific attention was devoted to assigning responsibility for installation and operation, to increasing work force involvement in the implementation stages, and to establishing reasonable timetables. This phase required almost six months.

The third phase focused on installation and debugging. Since the system was too large to be implemented simultaneously in all areas, priorities were established, and a sequenced program was formulated. Vendors were selected, construction of the data base was begun, hardware was installed, and software development was initiated. Provision was made for analysis and debugging time between each step. A detailed pert network served as one of the main control mechanisms. This phase took approximately two years, but it proceeded like clockwork. In spite of what may have seemed a leisurely pace and costly planning effort, this system became fully operational in less time and with less cost and disruption than many similar projects which are rushed through on crash bases.

The final phase was one of continued review and evaluation. It actually began near the start of the third phase and has been carried on since by a smaller, but still inter-disciplinary standing committee.

The starting point for comprehensive planning must be a clearly perceived statement of goals and objectives. This places a high premium on effective communications, especially in decentralized operations. Personal rewards must be structured so that they relate to contributions to over-all goal achievement.

Broad statements of objectives are usually inadequate decision guidelines. They must be refined to yield specific targets, and measures of effectiveness must be established and rigorously applied to the evaluation of specific proposals. For example, computer installations are often justified on the basis of "before and after" cost comparisons. Yet impartial critiques often reveal that the cost reductions derive not from the computer but from the preparatory work which is done to clean up operations in anticipation of the installation. Unless useful evaluative criteria and procedures are established, resources may be wasted.

One of the challenges for comprehensive planning stems from the fact that it is future-oriented, and we have not yet learned how to predict the future accurately. This applies both to changes in product and process technology and to chains of casuality.

Technology is changing faster than we can keep pace. Metal fabrications are replaced by unitary plastic moldings, mailed documents give way to facsimile transmission, air travel is supplanted by the closed circuit T.V. conference, and the manila file folder yields first to the magnetic core and then, perhaps, to the hologram. Technological forecasting methods often facilitate more accurate assessments of the probabilities of future developments. However, they tend to be more useful in projecting changes in operating parameters (e.g., the quantity of information which can be stored per unit of volume) than on predicting the physical natures of particular advancements (e.g., the configuration of the storage device).

Even if we could accurately predict future technology, we still have much to learn about developing techniques which enable us to predict the consequences of particular actions in environments as complex as those in which industrial firms operate. Much of the uncertainty we face comes from ignorance. At best, we can only assign probabilities to the likely outcomes of a decision. Often, to determine the consequences of a particular action, we must identify and analyze an enormous network of stochastic processes. Often this task exceeds both current knowledge of environmental interrelations and available computational capacities.

Input-output and computerized simulation models can be used to reduce environmental uncertainty. However, the value of these techniques is a direct function of the comprehensiveness of the model structure, the validity of the relationships between system elements, and the accuracy of the data inputs. (The same is true of technological forecasting models.) Often, the broader the inputs (at both the design and the data collection stages), the greater the probability of useful results.

The use of multifunctional teams, drawn from diverse disciplines, can be an invaluable asset for automation planning, not only because it may lead to widespread commitment, but also because it expands the range of factors which are likely to be considered. The introduction of a new piece of automatic machinery typically affects more than just the production process. It may affect human behavior and morale, management and worker skill requirements, materials, quality standards and costs. It may suggest the need for a new organizational structure, alter relationships with customers, and necessitate a rethinking of resource allocation procedures. Future production and product plans must be factored into the decision. The greater the knowledge and breadth of the planners, the smaller the likelihood that such factors will be overlooked.

The use of broad committees for automation planning has another, sometimes negative, but often positive consequence. It tends to apply brakes to the process and to reduce tendencies toward impulse automation, although a properly structured planning committee can still retain the flexibility required to move quickly. The rapid changes which occur in the industrial setting make it advisable to avoid long lead times lest projects become obsolete before they can be implemented. Managers become impatient, and often, when they undertake automation projects in areas where they have had little previous experience, timetables are based upon the judgements of vendors, many of whom seem to be either incurable optimists or something else. The focus is typically placed on the consequences of being late. Yet the consequences of underestimating the time factor can be severe, both in terms of dollars and morale. By exploring more of the issues (and in greater depth), interdisciplinary committees may offset a lemming-like rush into automation. They also increase the probability that major decisions will be implemented in steps, each of which provides the benefits of the learning curve to subsequent activities.

Commitment – A Key

A key problem faced in automating is the question of responsibility. The installation of new production equipment coupled to a control computer may involve a machinery vendor, a computer firm, conveyor manufactures, the telephone company, instrument suppliers, and a host of electrical, plumbing and masonry contractors. Turn-key contracts are not always available or even desirable. Without clear identification of responsibilities, a company can find that the only response it receives from its vendors with respect to systems' problems is the formation of a ring, a-la-Mast, with each contractor pointing his finger at another. Comprehensive planning will not eliminate this possibility, but it is more likely to identify the problem in advance and to result in the establishment of procedures for assigning responsibility.

Unless the support of the people who are going to operate and use a system can be obtained, rough weather lies ahead. The interdisciplinary planning task force, by virtue of its large membership, generates a high degree of involvement per se. However, it is also more likely to result in widespread involvement outside of the group, and involvement is the first step to commitment.

One of the most effective methods for obtaining commitment is to bring the individuals who are going to operate the system into the final planning and the very early installation and debugging stages.

One company which asked its machinists to help plan for the introduction of automatic equipment found that they had very valuable ideas to contribute which reduced installation time and improved operations substantially. Furthermore, the machinists became so caught-up in the installation phase that most learned how to perform their own maintenance work. The company was delighted to restructure work assignments and pay levels (at the machinists' request) so that they could look after their own equipment.

A large department store involved its sales personnel in a similar manner with the implementation of a computerized data collection and managerial-decision-assisting system. It also found the same type of positive results, although a sister firm which introduced an almost identical system informing each employee via a series of short briefing sessions, experienced great difficulty.

A substantial benefit from such involvement is that it tends to minimize rumors. Uncertainty about the future is reduced; misconceptions about the impact of automation can be avoided; uncertainty about future job security can be diminished — especially important in situations where management has no intention of firing employees.

Another benefit is that the involvement of employees from the start automatically results in the initiation of training activities. One of the primary effects of automation is a change in skill requirements. The old style production planner may have to become a programming specialist. The maintenance man who formerly qualified as an electrician may now have to qualify as an electronics specialist. Controlled environments give rise to needs for air conditioning and humidity control specialists. Although the net result may be no decrease in employment levels (on the contrary, decreases in employment due to automation seem to occur in those industries which fail to keep pace, not in those which are on the forefront), some retraining or restructuring of work requirements will probably be required. Telling a man that he is assured of a job may not be enough. He may be unsure of his ability to learn a new task. An early start on the training process provides a more supportive transition period.

Early involvement of the workforce requires planning. Time must be provided to free workers from present duties during the installation phases without bringing existing production to a halt. Sometimes training must be started far in advance of installation. Tests may have to be administered to determine who is capable of making the transition, and positions may have to be found for the workers who cannot adapt to the change. Assurances must be provided when skills have to be imported from outside. This takes time and must be thought through in advance.

One of the basic characteristics of comprehensive planning is that it is an ongoing effort, incorporating numerous feedback loops. Because the

industrial environment changes rapidly, and because it takes time to implement any planned procedures, a company may discover, in the middle of a
well thought through program, that it is dealing with a whole new situation. The planners must be sensitive to such changes, and must be able to
adapt. Probably the most important characteristic they must possess is the
willingness to regard everything which has preceded as a sunk cost.

At periodic intervals or evaluation points, current goals and objectives
must be matched with environmental conditions and new priorities must
be established. In some cases, the analysis will show the need to redo much
of what has already been done. In others, there will be little alteration of
the existing plan. Such periodic planning analysis and review procedures
help insure that organizational objectives are continuously in step with
environmental conditions, that effective criteria are available to facilitate
the evaluation of alternate courses of action, and that an up-to-date map is
accessible to all levels of the enterprise. These iterative planning procedures also provide the benefit of documentation which greatly assists future
planning efforts.

Transition To The Macro Level

The value of comprehensive planning at the micro level can be clearly
demonstrated by comparing the results achieved by companies which use
the approach with those of firms which do not. The benefits of establishing clear understandings of goals and objectives, of treating the enterprise and its environment as a system of interlinked elements, and of
reducing suboptimzation are similarly apparent at the enterprise level.

When we pull back so that our lens views a broader spectrum of activity, the national economy for instance, a series of interesting transforma-
tions takes place. First, the situation increases in complexity by many
orders of magnitude. Second, in our "wide angle" view, the individual firm
tends to lose its identity and becomes just one of a number of small dots
which, in the aggregate, comprise the scene before us. Finally, we
encounter a negative change in attitude toward planning.

One of the most important consequences of the transition from the
micro to the macro level is that no matter how comprehensive the planning of individual enterprises, the aggregate affect may be that of
Brownian movement. The economy may expand, but by a basically random process. Activities of many units will tend to cancel one another, and
the direction of motion becomes largely a function of the new applications

of technology which emerge and the resources which are available to develop them. Suboptimization becomes a way of life — a way which, until recently, we naively assumed would lead to system optimization.

We are only beginning to realize that our country and our planet contain limited resources. Perhaps more than anything else, the pictures of the earth taken from the surface of the moon have reinforced the idea that we live on a space ship, a closed system moving through the vacuum which surrounds us. Pressures deriving from the geometric growth of population and the increase in per capita expectations of goods and services make our world an even tighter system. Recent developments in methods of transportation and communication shrink the environment even further. We may be reaching a stage analogous to Saturday morning in the bargain basement of a large urban department store — where you cannot raise an elbow without poking someone in the ribs.

The lack of comprehensive planning at the macro level gives rise to the same kinds of problems which occur when we examine the individual firm, except that they affect many more people and environmental factors. However, two seem especially critical. First, many actions taken at the micro level (and which seem sensible from that vantage point) actually suboptimize to the detriment of other elements of the system and to the system as a whole. Second, resources are often expended inefficiently.

Inefficient Use of Resources

The lack of planning and coordination shows up dramatically in the patchwork "systems" which have evolved at the macro level. Again, transportation provides an example. First we developed ships to move goods over the seas. Then we developed railroads to move them over land. But these forms were not flexible or fast enough, so we added to the patchwork quilt, highways and vehicular traffic, and then airlines. Each was developed and operated independently of the others. Only when the pressures began to mount did we go back and attempt to make the pieces fit. For example, by putting freight into containers which can be transferred from one form to another, or by the development of the piggy-back concept. But the introduction of these changes has required much undoing of the past. Furthermore, the changes have been obstructed by many of our antiquated social institutions such as the rail and shipping rate structures and the jurisdictional infighting of some of the unions. We seem to resist the notion that technological change requires social change and that the organization of functions is intimately related to the nature of those functions.

Air transportation — man's most recent development in the automation of walking — provides another example of inefficient resource utilization. Today we have commercial aircraft capable of traveling faster than the speed of sound; however, in many situations we have lost much of the benefit of this speed. First we built the planes and the airports. Then the airports became crowded and technically obsolete, so we now build bigger airports which are located further from the cities and take longer to reach. Baggage handling facilities become overburdened, and parking problems increase as air traffic continues to expand. Planes stack up over the airports, and costs rise. Consequently we build bigger aircraft, which exacerbate problems on the ground. We become locked into a situation where much of our time and energy must be devoted to correcting the current crises or postponing impending ones. Soon the airplane starts to lose its effectiveness, and the great speed of the plane is offset by the time wasted getting to and from the airport, by the seemingly endless circling in holding patterns, and by the long waits for baggage. We start to regress to the point where a trip from Boston to New York often can be made more quickly by a car capable of traveling at only a tenth the speed of the plane. When the highways eventually jam up, we may be able to take consolation in the fact that we will not have to regress all the way back to using our feet because we may still be able to use the horse.

Planning at the Macro Level

Why do we accept the need for planning at the micro level and tend to reject it at the macro? Few individuals would argue that a company should not set goals and objectives and establish plans to carry them out — plans which can be promulgated in manners which are consistent with concepts of decentralized decision making. Yet feelings toward planning at state or national levels are often very negative.

The nature of the planning problems we face at the macro level is very much like that found at the micro. The same ingredients are needed. Without some type of comprehensive approach, the result can be a society that functions by processes akin to impulse automation. Sometimes we guess right and sometimes we do not. But the magnitude of many of the problems is becoming so great, both physically and/or perceptually, that we cannot afford many more wrong guesses. We already have too many bruised ribs.

8

Some Manpower Implications

Edgar Weinberg

THE PAST DECADE has seen a remarkable evolution in the public's attitudes about the manageability of automation. Ten years ago, the coming
of automation was regarded as a serious threat to job security. Unemployment was 6 percent of the labor force. Some observers forecasted mass
labor displacement as computers took over routine tasks. Others predicted
a drastic decline of manufacturing as a source of jobs similar to the displacement that had taken place in agriculture. The accelerating pace of
change, the explosion of knowledge and the computer revolution — the
terms used to describe modern technology — created a sense of rapid
obsolescence of skills among all ranks of society. Some doubted that
management of the consequences of automation, which was used synony-
mously with all technological change, could be made within the existing
economic framework.

Today, there is less fear about the effects of automation. The predictions of the pessimists have not been borne out. Technology has proved to
be a source of new jobs as well as a source of displacement. Unemployment is lower, public and private planning for handling manpower problems is more extensive, and there is confidence that automation will not
cause such severe dislocation that it cannot be managed within the existing
social system. Whether this more positive attitude is permanent remains to
be seen. A keen student of technology once said that "the ratio between
those who hail our continuing technical progress and those who deplore
the advancing encroachment of the machine is an excellent index of the
current position in the business cycle."

This paper reviews some manpower implications of automation from
the broad program concerns of government. Automation is considered a
continuation of the historic process of mechanization and technological
change, in which human effort has been transferred to machines. It deals
first with the pace of technological change and then considers the three

manpower issues that must be considered if the benefits of new technology are to be fully realized: the maintenance of employment growth, the improvement of education and training and the adjustments by management and workers for the orderly introduction of change.

Pace of Technological Change

First, the pace of technological change is important to consider because it is an indicator of the extent of dislocation that may occur. Journalists use freely the phrase, "accelerating pace of change," as if they had a meaningful indicator. Measurement of the rate of technological change, however, presents many difficulties of concept and data. In terms of scientific discovery, it is undeniable that the pace has quickened, with one spectacular advance leading to another. The quadrupling of funds for research and development, the doubling of the number of scientists and engineers in the past 15 years and the great proliferation of technical publications lend credence to the idea of a knowledge explosion. Since a considerable part of the "industry of discovery" is related to defense and space technology, its growth may be a slowing down. Even so, R and D will remain an immense source of change.

The rate of development and diffusion of new technology is more uncertain. If we consider change as an evolutionary process, beginning with invention and extending to widespread use of a specific machine, then we can compare the time taken to reach critical milestones to determine if the process is accelerating. Although the data are extremely skimpy, they suggest some shortening at least of the development stage. In a study of 20 major inventions for the National Commission on Technology, Automation and Economic Progress, Frank Lynn found that the time for developing inventions to point of commercial usage had shortened remarkably. Lynn's list of course included only successful innovations and took no account of inventions that failed commercial introduction. The evidence on the rate of diffusion is less clear. Professor Edwin Mansfield for the same Commission studied the time it took 12 different innovations to spread from company to company in 4 industries and found no clearcut evidence of a speed up.

Clearly, more research on the current rate of development and diffusion is badly needed. No doubt spectacular changes are taking place more rapidly today than in the past under pressure of massive government demand and support. The lunar landing only one decade after it was first programmed is an outstanding example of rapid development in the Era of

Big Science. But are such impressive achievements typical of the civilian market sectors? Some innovations have been adopted relatively slowly. For example, numerically controlled machine tools total only 16,000 or so, less than 1 percent of all machine tools, 15 years after being placed on the market. Nor have gas turbine engines, irradiated food, or synthetic leather displaced older products to the extent originally expected.

The most useful indicator of technological change is in terms of one of its principal results — the *increase in labor productivity.* The trend in output per man-hour is a comprehensive measure that takes account not only the change in the stock of technological knowledge but also of factors that influence its rate of application. It reflects, therefore, investment in new plant and equipment, improved skills of workers and managers, the state of labor relations and all other tangible and intangible forces that impinge on the effective use of technology.

The statistical record suggests no striking discontinuity in the economy performance. First, contrary to many forecasts in the early 1960's, there is no clear-cut evidence of acceleration in productivity growth during the 1960's. The Bureau of Labor Statistics indexes cover only the private economy; the productivity of government services being excluded for

OUTPUT PER MAN-HOUR AND OUTPUT IN THE PRIVATE NONFARM ECONOMY, 1950-69

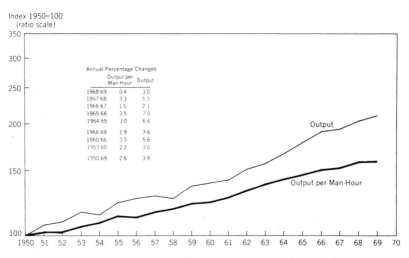

Index 1950=100 (ratio scale)

Annual Percentage Changes	Output per Man Hour	Output
1968-69	0.4	3.0
1967-68	3.3	5.3
1966-67	1.6	2.1
1965-66	3.5	7.0
1964-65	3.0	6.6
1966-69	1.9	3.6
1960-66	3.5	5.6
1950-60	2.2	3.0
1950-69	2.6	3.9

The slower growth in output since 1966 has been accompanied by a slower growth in productivity. The 1969 rise in productivity was the smallest since 1956.

various conceptual and statistical reasons. The increase for the private nonfarm economy averaged about 2.6 percent a year over the 1950-69 period. If we include the farm sector in our figures, the average rate for the total private economy jumps to 3.1 percent a year because of the high rate of gain in agriculture, amounting to 5.2 percent a year. This is significantly higher than the 2 percent rate of increase in nonfarm industry for the 1907-47 period which was marked by several periods of depression.

The growth rate, however, has been rather uneven. It averaged 2 percent a year in the nonfarm sector over the 1950-60 period, rose sharply to 3.5 percent a year for 1960-65, and then fell to 2.2 percent for 1965-69. The percent increase between 1968 and 1969 was unusually small, amounting to only 0.4 percent in private nonfarm and 0.9 percent in the private economy as a whole — the smallest increase in 13 years. This small improvement reflects primarily the reduced rate of capacity utilization that began in the late 1960's as the growth of real output was dampened. It should not be considered evidence of a permanent slowdown. As output resumes its expansive trend, the productivity growth rate will no doubt return to normal. The high level of capital spending and the continued improvement in the labor force's level of education, all portend continued long-term growth.

OUTPUT PER MAN-HOUR, COMPENSATION PER MAN-HOUR AND UNIT LABOR COSTS, PRIVATE NONFARM ECONOMY, 1950-69

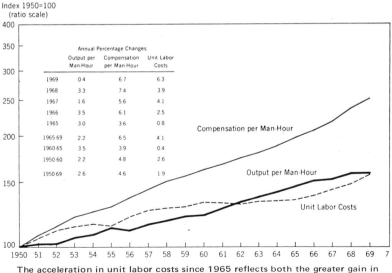

The acceleration in unit labor costs since 1965 reflects both the greater gain in compensation per hour and the slower rise in productivity.

Second, the overall figures do not necessarily represent the trend for individual industries. Although some growth takes place in almost every industry, not simply a few progressive ones, there are significant variations. For example, over the 1957-67 period such diverse industries as petroleum refining, air transportation and radio and TV manufacturing registered rates over 6 percent a year. On the other hand, footwear and cigarettes had a rate of gain of less than 2 percent a year. Basic steel, autos, and paper were in the 2-5 percent range.

Third, productivity in the United States has grown more slowly than in other industrial countries, despite our leadership in automation. The rate of gain in manufacturing between 1950 and 1969 averaged 2.9 percent a year in the U.S., which was less than one-third the average percent increase in Japan, and less than one-half the rate of advance in Italy and in the Netherlands. While this disparity may reflect recovery from low levels following wartime devastation, in some cases there has been even an increase since 1965. These figures do not mean that the level of output per manhour is higher in these countries. U.S. productivity still generally exceeds the level in other countries by a substantial margin but the gap may be closing.

Fourth, the low rate of productivity growth should be compared with changes in wages and labor costs, to understand fully its economic significance. This relationship has changed in important ways during the past decade. During the early 1960's, compensation per man-hour increased only slightly faster than productivity. As a result, unit labor costs remained at a fairly steady level. Beginning in 1965, there was a sharp divergence: compensation per man-hour rose sharply, at 6.5 percent a year, while output per man-hour increased at a much slower pace — 2.2 percent a year. Consequently, unit labor costs rose substantially. This rise could have the effect of encouraging employers to substitute laborsaving and other machinery to reduce their costs.

Finally, compared with trends in other countries, the rise in unit labor costs in U.S. manufacturing has been much higher. Although wage gains in most other countries have exceeded the U.S. gains since 1965 and for earlier periods, substantial productivity growth abroad has largely offset wage rises. Actually, unit labor costs in other countries have been fairly stable while ours have been increasing.

What is likely to be the pace of technological change in the future? One can cite an impressive list of innovations that presumably could boost productivity. Since the time it usually takes for a new development to have a widespread effect is about a decade or so, many of the changes that will influence the 70's are probably already in an early stage of commercial use. A few years ago, the Bureau of Labor Statistics investigated trends in 40 major industries to determine the important innovations of the next

GROWTH IN OUTPUT PER ALL EMPLOYEE MAN-HOUR IN SELECTED INDUSTRIES, 1960-68

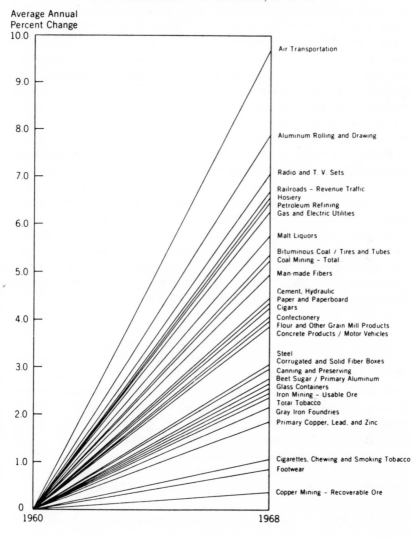

decade. Each industry had its own story and it was not always in terms of computer technology and automation. Materials handling and mechanization through higher speeds were often the major developments. Small improvements in auxiliary equipment often contribute to the cumulative growth of machine productivity.

While many developments are technically feasible, they are not necessarily economically profitable. The profitability of an innovation, the size of investment required, and the rate of capacity utilization act as an economic governor on the speed of diffusion. In some industries, institutional arrangements effectively bar needed improvements. For example, in the construction industry, the trend in output per man-hour, as far as we can determine, seems to lag behind manufacturing industry. It is possible that new industrialized methods could raise productivity significantly in building homes which are desperately needed. But the multiplicity of local building codes, the fragmentation of buyers, and the craft basis of unions raise barriers to mass production.

In short, the record is fairly reassuring about the extent of dislocation that can result from increases in labor productivity. No startling breakthroughs have taken place or are expected. Indeed, in the years ahead, it will be necessary to exploit more fully the potential of new technology such as industrial robots to improve our productive capacity and our world position. But as physical strength is delegated to industrial robots, the real issues become those of human adjustment to changing technology: sufficiency of demand to maintain a high level of employment; the education and training of workers for the new type of knowledge jobs; and the development of orderly methods of adjustment to change.

Impact on Employment

Resistance to innovations often comes from fear of loss of jobs or "technological unemployment." This attitude has been expressed sometimes in unexpected ways. There is the case of Walter Hunt, the New Yorker who invented the sewing machine but failed to patent it because he feared the displacement of seamstresses. In the depths of the 1930's depression, a leading Congressman proposed a moratorium on the issuance of patents on the grounds that laborsaving machinery was responsible for mass unemployment. Had this excessive concern prevailed, economic stagnation would have imperiled our survival in the 1940's.

The amount of "technological unemployment" cannot be measured because the effects of change are so complex, indirect and diffused. Technological change does not appear in isolation but is modified and mixed with other sources of change, such as shifts in consumer taste, population growth, and international competition. Furthermore, the effects of technological change do not necessarily occur at the site of the change but are diffused through the mechanism of competition to other plants and industries throughout the economy.

There is abundant evidence in the experience of the 1960's that steady technical advance is quite compatible with rising employment as long as the economy is buoyant and demand is advancing. Productivity increase in every year between 1961 and 1969 but output increased even more. Employment rose steadily. More than 17 million workers were added to nonfarm payrolls between early 1961 and the end of 1969 — a 30 percent increase. Furthermore, the output increase was sufficiently large to offset not only the productivity increase but also the growth in the labor force. Accordingly, unemployment declined from 6.7 percent in 1961 to 3.5 percent in 1969.

Although a high level of total demand can go a long way toward reducing overall unemployment to a minimum, it cannot prevent labor from being displaced from particular industries, plants or occupations. Output does not advance at the same rate as productivity in all industries or plants and consequently some register employment declines. Inefficient plants are shut down and workers laid off. The classic cases are agriculture, railroads and coal mining. When the industry is concentrated in a particular region or locality, a depressed area could be created. In a dynamic economy, however, the highly mobile labor displaced from declining activities become the manpower supply for expanding industries.

Some displaced workers have much greater difficulty than others in finding new jobs. According to studies of worker displacement made over the past 40 years, Negroes, older workers, unskilled and women workers experience much longer periods of unemployment than others and suffer greater losses in wages. In the 1960's, some economists argues that the complex nature of automation creates even greater barriers for the unskilled and uneducated, and the structurally unemployed would remain a large group even in periods of high economic growth. Fortunately, experience did not completely confirm their prediction. As the economy expanded during the 1960's, unemployment rates among all groups declined, with sharp reductions occurring among the lesser skilled. Apparently the normal operation of the labor market produced some accommodation between the skills possessed by workers and those required by employers.

Despite the general improvement, a sizeable number of persons — about 2.9 million on the average in 1969 — are unemployed even in a period of substantial demand for labor. The number who are "technologically unemployed" is unknown for the reasons explained earlier. New data about the reasons for unemployment suggest that it is probably a small percent of the total. In 1969, nearly two-thirds of the unemployed reported leaving their previous job voluntarily, reentering the labor market, or entering for the first time. Only 35 percent reported having lost their last job, some no doubt for technological reasons.

While the major part of unemployment cannot be attributed to "technological displacement," it is conceivable that many of the teenagers and young adults who made up about half of the unemployed in 1969 lacked adequate preparation to enter work in a technological society. The wastage of skill, motivation and morale is doubly excessive in a period of inflationary pressures. The transition from school to work in a changing technology should be greatly improved if the high unemployment rate among young people is to be reduced.

Planning education and training based on realistic information about environment workers will be entering is an important step in assuring their proper adjustment to changing technology. What will be the requirements of tomorrow cannot be anticipated with certainty, but it is possible to develop reasonable approximations of the future by examining past trends and making assumptions about the key factors affecting employment. The Bureau of Labor Statistics develops systematic projections of the size of the labor force, the growth of the economy and the structure of jobs by correlating a large body of information on trends in technology, production, demand productivity, occupations and employment. These projections have been made for 1975 and are about to be published for 1980.

The dominant trend in the 1970's will be the continued growth of white collar employment as a result of the interaction between economic and technological factors. Increased productivity in the production of goods and related activities allows industry to satisfy the growing demand for goods with an increasingly smaller proportion of the work force. At the same time technological advances have not yet improved productivity, significantly so far as we can measure it, in the service industries. With demand for services such as education, health, and personal services, rising more rapidly than goods, as incomes increase, employment in the service sector has greatly expanded.

Both factors result in an occupational structure heavily weighted with white collar jobs. By 1975, requirements for professional, technical and related occupations will be 45 percent or 4 million greater than in 1965 and will employ 15 percent of the work force compared with 13 percent in 1965. Clerical and service jobs will be the second fastest growing groups, increasing about 33 percent; and sales workers, 25 percent. The blue collar jobs will be increasing more slowly: craftsmen, by 23 percent; operatives, by 10 percent; and laborers, will decline by 2 percent. Farmers and farm laborers will continue their long term decline, decreasing by 22 percent.

Some analysts see these trends leading to a "knowledge society," the "post industrial society," and the "service economy." These simplifications are useful insights but should not be interpreted to mean that workers with modest educational talents will have no opportunities. There will continue to be many routine jobs which are not yet economic to mechanize and many manual jobs, like postmen, which are too complex to automate. Interdependence of many different skills will remain a characteristic of the economy in the future as it has been in the past.

The content of jobs and the qualities required of workers will also be modified by technological changes. There will be relatively less demand for manual dexterity, physical strength for handling, and for traditional know-how and more stress on formal knowledge, precision and perceptual aptitudes. All jobs will probably be subject to more frequent changes and the average worker will need to be retrained for several different but probably related jobs during his working life. The diminution of deadening repetitive tasks that are so dissatisfying to the industrial worker may be welcomed but whether isolation and constant monitoring create new stresses remains to be studied.

In addition to the outlook for occupational structure, the Bureau of Labor Statistics is investigating the manpower impact of specific new technologies. Such information may be of practical use to plant managers and vocational schools in planning for the future. Currently, we are studying the implications of the computers in industrial applications such as process control and printing. Computer control of typesetting, for example, will greatly modify the jobs of compositors and require changes in training. The applications of computers to process control involves considerable knowledge of systems engineering. The diffusion of computer technology may depend more and more on the availability of adequately trained programers and systems analysts.

The most challenging opportunities will probably come from new industrial developments stemming from recent technological advances. New software firms, an industry of inquiry, and data banks are being organized around the computer, opening up opportunities for many types of data specialists. The creation of giant "nuplexes" combining nuclear power, desalination, metallurgical and chemical plants will require managers and technicians of great skill. Supersonic air transportation, picture phones and data phones will facilitate the expansion of the international corporation to all parts of the world.

As regional megolopolis like CHIPITTS, SANSAN, and BOSWASH emerge, the shortage of people to deal with complex urban problems will be even more acute. Finally, we need broad-gaged engineers who can assess the effects of these technological achievements on a higher systems level and design to protect the quality of the environment.

Technological and manpower trends reinforce the need for more formal education at all levels. Obviously, illiteracy is a crushing handicap in finding work in a technological society. Education of people receptive to and comfortable with change requires greater emphasis on basic academic skills up through high school. The National Commission on Technology, Automation and Economic Progress recommended the establishment of a nationwide system of free public education through 2 years beyond high school as a means of facilitating adjustment. Updating the curriculum of vocational schools, assuring college opportunities for all qualified individuals, and providing specialists with flexibility in case of obsolescence are some of the problems of preparing people for work in this age of changing technology.

Adjustment to Technological Change

Finally, what can be done at the plant for an orderly worker adjustment to technological change? If the costs of change can be reduced surely management will find less resistance to innovation. Formerly, lessening of the effects of labor displacement was left to the free play of the market. Today attitudes are different and people expect more. There has been a shift toward sharing the costs more widely so that they do not fall so heavily on some individuals while the community as a whole benefits. Government agencies, and the local communities, as well as labor and management, can contribute to cushioning the impact of change on the individual.

Private measures worked out by the parties immediately concerned are likely to be the principal means because of their great flexibility in meeting diverse cases. When management and labor representatives discussed adjustment problems at the Labor Department seminars in 1964, they all agreed on the necessity of considering individual circumstances such as the size of firm, the nature of the labor market and the economic processes causing displacement. For example, problems of technological change in a declining industry, differ from those in an expanding/multi-plant company. Different approaches must be developed to meet specific demands of the work force in terms of age, sex, skill, levels, basic education and location. Legislation could hardly take account of the great variety of circumstances.

There is no complete inventory of programs nor is there an estimate of how many persons are covered by adequate plans. Many of the well known programs such as the Armour plan, the West Coast Longshore agreement and the steel workers programs have been studied in depth. Some adjustments, such as those on the railroads, came about after lengthy study and bitter conflict. The Bureau of Labor Statistics has made several case studies of lesser known plans in the government, public utility and telephone industries.

From the experience of firms and unions five "shock absorbers" that can help soften the employment impact of automation can be sketched. The five mechanisms for adjustment described following stress the minimizing of the hardships of adjustment and layoff through advance notice, reliance on attrition, provision for job security, training and community cooperation. We cite these "social inventions" not as surefire prescriptions for all but simply as mechanisms that could contribute to a more orderly and less painful diffusion of new technology.

First, advance notice to workers, unions, and the community, especially in large scale displacement, has been repeatedly proven to be in the words of Professors Shultz and Weber, the "procedural prerequisite for constructive action." It provides time for affected individuals to formulate their own plans and to weigh carefully alternative jobs or layoff arrangements. Many companies that install computers take advantage of the long lead-time, often as long as one year, to explain to their employees the reasons for change and the possible impact. Some take great pains to state explicitly that affected employees would continue to have a job though not necessarily the one they occupied at the time of the change. Such advance notice lessens anxiety and resistance to change. In a few collective bargaining situations, advance notice has been the start of continuous joint study of basic issues and cooperative search for solutions.

Second, some companies have found that by coordinating manpower and technical planning they have a better chance to reduce their labor force by attrition, thereby avoiding sudden layoffs. In changing over to the dial system, for example, the telephone companies have long followed the practice of projecting their manpower requirements a year or two in advance. By controlling hiring of permanent employees and estimating its attrition rate, they minimize the amount of displacement at the time of the change. Some companies try to time the introduction of new technology to a period of business expansion to cushion the impact on employees.

Third, providing a variety of measures for job security or income maintenance is increasingly regarded as part of the cost of change. During the 1960's, collective bargaining featured severance pay, early retirement benefits, interplant transfer rights, relocation allowances and similar job security provisions. With price stability, it was easier for unions to win fringe benefits, than increases in wage rates. Because workers' needs differ according to age, family circumstances, etc., the availability of a choice among several different adjustment options has been found to be particularly helpful. Women workers, with family responsibilities, for example, are more likely to draw severance than take relocation allowances in case of a plant shutdown. More mobile younger workers may also prefer separation pay while older workers with seniority may wish to exercise rights to jobs in other company plants.

Fourth, modern technology requires an increasing amount of training. With the computer and similar complex equipment, management will find training becoming more formal, continuous, and costly, but essential to keep the work force up to date and flexible. Arbitrary notions about the trainability of older workers which recent research challenges may need to be reexamined. Some labor experts envisage businesses of the future as partially educational institutions and see collective bargaining expanding in the 1970's into the field of education benefits as it did in the pension field in the 1960's. Making available learning opportunities at any age could diminish resistance to change and hasten the diffusion of new technology with a minimum of hardship.

Finally, the cooperation of private management with government and community agencies is essential to assist displaced workers to find new jobs with a minimum period of unemployment. With the beginning of the Manpower Development and Training program, a more active manpower policy was established at the local and national levels. Displaced workers can now obtain a wide range of services to improve their employability: job counselling and training, up to date occupational information, and an early warning system in case of mass layoff. If notified before shut down, the local employment office can furnish testing and placement services to workers while still working. The U.S. Training and Employment Service is developing a computerized placement service and job data banks which could speed up measureably the entire placement process.

Conclusion

To conclude, this discussion indicates that difficult as the problems of introducing automation may be they may yet be managed in a constructive way with the cooperation of all concerned. There is no reason to expect that the pace of change will require drastic departure from the existing social system. While there is need for improvements in administering changes within the office or plant, it is also important to recognize that problems may arise beyond the power of individual companies and their union to handle. A vital challenge is to assure economic growth in the 1970's at a pace sufficiently rapid to absorb workers displaced by technological change and those entering the labor market. The task will be greater than in the past because a much larger increase in the labor force is expected in the 1970's than during the 1960's.

The 1970's will probably see more attention given to improving the delivery of services by the educational system, job training programs, vocational guidance and counseling and placement offices. Public and private policies to maintain high level employment will be discussed. Accordingly, university centers, with government, labor and management will have to continue to keep watch on the course of automation and to assemble more information about its effects and control for the national welfare.

9

Management Attitudes Toward Automation

Russell A. Hedden

IN THIS DISCUSSION on management attitudes toward automation, I would like to begin at one of the points made during the 1969 Georgia-Reliance symposium. That point is the observation by Roger W. Bolz that "properly applied, automation makes possible desired goods and services at reasonable prices through two advantages: greater productivity without added labor and increased throughput."

That statement is basic to any examination of management attitudes towards automation because the leaders of industry accept it as an economic axiom. Bolz also observed in 1969 that automation fosters greater employment and is a strong social good.

This second point also is essential to this discussion because it recognizes a fundamental truth about our social and economic system: no force is allowed to exist in this system that creates permanent unemployment or which is antisocial in character.

In examining this subject it is desirable to first explore the human factors related to it because concern about automation is always expressed in terms of its effect on human beings. Then it is useful to review management awareness of the effects of automation before turning to the question of planning and planning approaches. The positive economic and social characteristics of automation will emerge from this examination.

What Is Meant By Automation?

First it is necessary to establish what is meant by automation. The most popular definition, and the most widely accepted, is that automation is some form of self-regulation or automatic control.

At the risk of over-simplification, automation can be more broadly defined as the use of better tools so we can produce more goods with less work. What is more, automation in one form or another is the only way in which we can increase our productivity and the wages per man hour of labor without increasing the cost of the product and thereby reduce the size of the market that can be served.

It was progress in automation which has brought us to our current high standard of living. Technological evolution through the centuries has brought us from the very earliest days when it was a full-time job for a man growing and hunting enough food to keep him alive to our current society in which we spend more time in leisure than we do in work.

But throughout the industrial revolution and its subsequent evolution, automation has been criticized as the harbinger of mass unemployment and the dehumanizer of the working man. This attitude has led to violent reactions throughout history.

A mob in Germany in the 1660's drowned the inventor of a mechanized loom. Steam engines and power machinery were frequently smashed in 19th Century England. And in the 1920's in our own country, we heard claims that mechanization and the use of electrical machinery would ruin the economy.

The advent of computers and numerical control technology has prompted similar concerns. Twenty years ago an MIT professor predicted that automatic machines "will produce an unemployment situation in comparison with which ... the depression of the thirties will seem a pleasant joke."

These fears are becoming very pronounced again with the advances in automatic machine tool control technologies, and their rapid adoption. There are today more than 15,000 numerical control systems operating in U.S. factories and new systems are being added at the rate of 4,000 to 5,000 each year. Sophisticated adaptive control and direct computer control systems are realities now, and we are beginning to see the installation of plantwide computer control and computer monitoring systems.

Earlier this year a group of European computer experts released a report that implied the same dire predictions. They forecast that by the late 1980's there will be a 50 percent reduction in the working force in present industries which shorter working hours and new industries will only partly absorb. Consequently, they said unemployment is expected to be a serious problem.

This grim spectre also conjures up the other concern about automation; that it dehumanizes the worker, relegating him to a faceless existence and depriving him of his individuality. This same concern has existed throughout the history of industrialization.

Apprehensions Unfounded

In dispelling these apprehensions, merely examine the charge that automation is killing off jobs. Back in the mid-50's when the automation concern was reviving, some people were claiming that automation was killing off jobs at the rate of 40,000 a week. At the time there were a little over 60 million people employed in the United States and about 3-1/2 million unemployed.

Today after some 15 years of constantly increasing automation there are over 78 million people employed and a half-million fewer people listed as unemployed. So instead of losing 40,000 jobs a week, we have added about 23,000 each week.

Many jobs are eliminated of course from many unpredictable causes, including automation. The Labor Department has estimated the loss at about 1-1/2 million each year. But at the same time, 2-1/2 to 3-1/2 million new jobs are being created by our expanding economy so there is a net gain in job opportunities.

The question of whether automation dehumanizes the worker is a little more difficult to answer because it can be dealt with only in essentially subjective terms. However, this contention is equally as baseless as the allegation that automation leads to mass permanent unemployment.

In fact, the best, most concise description of automation is that it is the human use of human beings. That phrase first used by Norbert Weiner which sums up the true promise of automation — the human use of human beings — that is the antithesis of the complaint that automation robs the worker of his identity.

In support of this observation, consider these facts: first, the jobs which are automated first in a factory are those which are the easiest to automate because they are the most repetitive and mechanical, and the least human. Secondly, management automates those tasks which are potentially dangerous for the worker, or which subject their employees to unhealthy or uncomfortable working conditions because those conditions are inefficient and generate internal strife and unrest.

But, even accepting the arguments against long-term permanent unemployment and dehumanization, critics of automation inevitably warn management that their workforce will be severely disrupted by the shock of sudden economic changes and the abrupt elimination of jobs within their respective plants. These arguments are especially prevalent in recent years because we do indeed appear to be approaching a true automated factory as a practical reality.

But these claims too have erupted throughout history. In 1929, a Committee on Recent Economic Changes observed that "Each generation believes itself to be on the verge of a new economic era, an era of fundamental change." Ours is not the first era to experience profound changes in technology, and the economy has survived similar assaults in the past.

Uniform Pace of Change

When Mr. Bolz was editor-in-chief of Automation magazine a few years ago, he wrote that "in today's busy world it is widely accepted that technology is moving at a dizzying pace — but this is mostly on paper. The real pace of change is far more uniform and gradual than many would like to admit. And this is especially true of automation. The technology is being applied at a rather modest rate almost exclusively as economic and market needs demand."

But it is true that the workforce within a specific plant or industry can be severely disrupted when a process or operation is automated. In these cases, management's attitude is universal, I am sure, in doing everything possible to absorb the displaced worker and retrain him for other necessary duties.

There are several factors to be considered in this question of worker displacement. Many jobs normally are not automated until management can no longer perform the function with trained personnel; and the operation is automated only when it can be demonstrated that it is more economical to automate rather than train a new operator, or when the demands on the operator place the function beyond human capability.

Automation also is undertaken as a rule when the business of a plant is on the upswing so the expanding activities usually open new jobs in other departments or operations within the factory. This absorption of displaced workers usually is done very easily because the displaced employees represent a minimal percentage of the plant's workforce.

Another factor is that industry has always had a difficult time in filling its needs for skilled labor, reinforcing the contention that our expanding technology creates more jobs than it destroys.

Labor Department statistics, for example, show that only about one-third of the unemployed in 1969 had lost their previous jobs involuntarily. The rest had either quit, were re-entering the labor market or had never worked before. Consider too that during the last recession, unemployment among unskilled workers soared to 14 percent while the rate for highly skilled workers hardly rose above 2 percent.

I think it is a well-known fact that job training programs within industry have existed for decades because management realizes the universal need for trained workers. After all, industry must serve its own ends and a ready supply of skilled workers is a necessity.

Labor Department forecasts for the 1970's indicate the continued and growing need for trained employees. The department says the need for skilled and semi-skilled workers will continue to grow while no expansion is foreseen in jobs for the unskilled despite the population growth.

So the demand for job training and retraining programs will continue to grow on a par with the demand for trained employees. There is evidence of increased training investments by management at all skill levels, from production workers, through middle management to the professional job level.

At Bendix for example our investment in tuition support programs for salaried people has doubled in the last four years, and I feel certain our industry experience regarding shop training programs for hourly rated employees is comparable.

Two other human factors mentioned as sources of concern are the community in which a plant is located, and management apprehension about the unsettling results of automation.

Enlightened top management should be able to avoid problems in either area by maintaining communications programs citing the social and economic benefits of automation as they apply to the employees residing in the community and to management personnel involved in carrying out automation programs.

Management Awareness

This leads to the next topic — management awareness of the effects of automation. This subject might better be explored as management's awareness of the need for automation because I believe it is incumbent upon the management of any concern hoping to compete successfully to be fully aware of the economics of automation.

There are four major points to be considered. First and most important, the equipment-labor-productivity ratios. Then the needs for repeatability and reliability, and finally the lack of trained people to do the job, forcing management to automate. We have already explored this last point, but again it is claimed if the telephone companies had not automated there would not be enough women in the entire country to handle the current volume of telephone calls manually.

The equipment-labor-productivity ratios dictate the need for better tools to increase our output per manhour and thereby lower cost. Lowered cost coupled with quality is essential to the success of any business competing today, but it is even more important to us as a nation if we hope to compete in the world market. We already have lost ground in many industries — consider shipbuilding, shipping and fishing, and unless we can maintain our productivity we are going to fall seriously behind economically. Take the automotive industry for example. The Toyota Motor Company of Japan has been increasing its productivity at an annual rate of 14 to 19 percent and today Toyota employees are the most productive auto workers in the world, producing $44,000 annually in sales per employee. By comparison, General Motor sales per employee were about $30,000 in 1969 and Volkswagen, $20,000.

James M. Roche, chairman of General Motors, said recently that the only way this nation can realize its lofty national goals — which are led by our many ambitious social and environmental projects — is to face up to the national crisis of cost. The only basis for a rising standard of material well-being is rising national productivity, he said, and the only way to achieve this is to "restore the balance that is lost between wages and productivity."

Labor costs are rising faster than productivity and equipment costs, according to Department of Labor statistics. The output per man-hour and the compensation per man-hour increased on a par from 1959 through 1965, and labor costs paralleled equipment prices from 1954 to 1962. This reflected a pretty stable economic situation with costs and prices changing as little as one percent.

But since 1963 labor costs have been rising faster than the cost of machinery, and the output per man-hour lagged well behind the cost of labor from 1965 through 1969. Incidentally, part of the reason for that ratio change has been a decline in the availability of labor.

Mr. Roche mentioned several factors which contribute to improving those ratios, including labor cooperation and improved design and materials. But increased usage of automation — better machines and tools and more efficient manufacturing methods — are among the strongest prescriptions management can take.

We have a classic example of the value of automation at Bendix. One of our divisions is a long-established name in bicycle brake production. But in 1958, we sold only 112,000 bicycle brakes, the lowest sales since World War II and our employment was down to 130. European and Japanese manufacturers were selling bicycle brakes at well below prices that were absolutely "rock bottom" for us.

Then we decided to get on the favorable side of the bicycle brake productivity ratio. Our brake was redesigned, we made a number of other changes — but most importantly, we automated. The first effect of auto- mation was the elimination of six jobs. The second noticeable effect was that we began to get back some of the business we had lost to foreign competition. We built four times as many brakes in 1960 as we had in 1958. Last year we sold 3.5 million bicycle brakes, compared to the 112,000 for 1958 and employment in that department is about 150. So automation kept us in the bicycle business and preserved 150 jobs. If we had not automated, we would have gone out of business just as our two leading American competitors had done.

The other two factors which point management towards increased automation — repeatability and reliability — are dictated by the needs of today's markets.

The demand for interchangeable parts that meet close tolerances and for reliable methods of repeating part specifications precisely can only be met automatically. A manually-operated machine simply cannot achieve the rates and accuracy demanded for identical production cycles.

An even more insistent pressure for automation is applied by the demand for increased product reliability. Automatic inspection techniques are the only way we can assure ourselves of 100 percent quality because judgments by human inspectors simply are not reliable enough. Only machines can be depended upon to devote full attention to the task at hand and only automatic machinery will continue to run at a constant level of operation without monitoring. Manually operated 100 percent inspection equipment must either stop when the operator takes a break, or an operator of equal ability must be substituted, which raises the cost per piece.

This area of quality based on improved inspection techniques has been benefitting immeasurably from automation. Another Bendix experience can be cited as an example. At one of our plants we had been employing 13 women and a supervisor to keep records on 104,000 gages used in various control operations. Because of the bulk of the material, the women often could not complete the job in the allotted eight hours and their accuracy left something to be desired.

When we computerized the function the machine did it in 15 minutes and with 100 percent accuracy. At the same time, the machine came up with important additional information that we were able to use to reduce the number of inspections required for each gage.

Additional information is not the only benefit of advanced automatic gaging techniques. Management is recognizing that advanced computer-aided gaging techniques can now check flaws that in the past were completely beyond the physical capabilities of human inspectors. Pattern recognition methods, for example, permit us to detect surface flaws which a visual inspection would completely overlook.

Automation Must Be Planned

To be most effective for a company, automation must be carefully planned and today's industrial management generally is taking the proper preparatory steps. This assessment is based largely in personal observations and the success automation has enjoyed as a driving force behind the expansion of our economy. A look at the research and development investments by our nation tend to support this observation because industry performs about 70 percent of all research and we can assume that an appreciable amount of that research is devoted to advanced industrial methods and processes.

Although there have been many cases of companies that invested heavily in automated equipment only to price their operations out of the market because of poor planning, knowledgeable business managers as a rule are extremely conservative in their decisions to automate operations since it usually requires heavy capital investment. Usually the decision is based on very careful evaluations of such factors as the return on investment potential offered by the outlay, the labor cost saving as compared to the investment and operating expense of the new equipment, and the degree of perfection the operation demands — do warranty and tolerance requirements demand the precision of automatic operations?

The decision also must be based on realistic forecasts of the future of the part to be produced. Will the demand for it survive long enough to pay for the investment in equipment? Will the automated operation be convertible to the production of similar or related parts that can be produced on the same equipment without extensive retooling? Then once these factors have been analyzed in the overall financial plan of the business the execution of the investment is carried out on a very careful priority basis.

The most practical approach to anticipating technological changes and planning subsequent automation of a production process is to give this function top priority. At Bendix, we long-ago recognized the value of anticipating innovations and *have assigned company officers* the responsibility of studying our manufacturing processes. These executives and their staffs monitor and analyze the processes and production costs at our plants, recommend improvements, and advise plant officials on the best way to carry out these improvements.

From this discussion, I am sure the positive social and economic values of automation have emerged. Management's attitude has always been based primarily on productivity and profit factors but it has been obvious over the years that those economic factors and the social considerations are virtually inseparable. When productivity declines and the economy sags, all facets of our society suffer because unemployment goes up and funds for social programs dwindle. An ambitious training program for hard-core unemployed had to be shelved last month by Chrysler because of the current mini-recession. It is evident that we are dependent upon the highest degree of automation if we are to maintain maximum employment and productivity, if we are to have the funds necessary for achieving our national social and environmental goals.

Workers will have to adjust to new tasks, but it is the nature of these new tasks that holds the real promise of automation. They are tasks which will free the worker from the deadly drudgery of the routine job that requires little skill and less alertness. Contrary to the past fears, man is finally becoming the master of the machine instead of just a part of it. We are about to put our human beings to a genuinely human use.

10

Implementing Automation

John J. McNiff

WITH THE DECISION TO IMPLEMENT a form of automation or advanced technology there frequently arises some very real concerns on the part of individual employees which should be considered by both labor and management. Although much of the following discussion shall be in the context of how labor organizations respond, the principles advanced are intended to be general in application and should not be limited to collective bargaining situations.

The subject range purposely has been expanded to include advanced technological change rather than limiting the review to automation in the precise sense, since the two are so closely allied in their effects on industrial relations.

It should be useful first to summarize the general reaction of labor organizations to the technological phenomena which have been grouped under the generic title of automation. The philosophy of most labor organizations was expressed most succinctly by the AFL-CIO in its publication, *Labor Looks at Automation:*

> "Technological change is inevitable. The hardships which it frequently causes are not. They occur partly because of national indifference and partly because those who introduce change are too often concerned only with what is technically possible and financially profitable. If an effort were made to make the new technology serve human needs, the hardships could be reduced to a minimum; technological change could proceed more smoothly; and in the long-run the benefits to all would be far greater."[1]

The general concern of labor is that improperly planned introduction of automation and advanced technological progress can lead to massive unemployment or result in severe hardship for some people and communities even in the absence of massive unemployment.

The consequences of rapid advances in productivity and increased growth in labor force are familiar to all who have been involved in our economy during the past fifteen years. Each year the pressure has increased on the economy to expand at a rate sufficient to absorb the growth in productivity and labor force. The ability of the economy to perform has been erratic at best.

Viewpoints of Labor

Labor organizations favor the use of taxing, spending, lending and other government powers to expand the economy at a rate sufficient to absorb all unavoidable unemployment, and to continue that expansion at an adjusted rate consistent with potential growth in productivity and the more rapid growth in the labor force expected during the Seventies. Concomitantly, labor organizations feel that the increased productivity and technological advances should be directed toward producing those goods and services which are in accord with a system of national priorities that will create new employment opportunities, improve earning capacity, distribute purchasing power more widely and improve the quality of American life in general.

While the general policy of labor organizations has been to place considerable emphasis on governmental action, this is not because they feel that the private sector is not responsible for its actions. Rather, this insistence on legislative response is a recognition of the fact that private industry individually or collectively may not be capable of fully performing the necessary effort which should accompany technological change. Thus, while employers who introduce new technology have an obligation to assist any of their employees who are displaced by such technology, the public – representing the wider social responsibility – must also provide a minimum level of adjustment assistance to those displaced in order to supplement private efforts and to avoid placing full cost on industry, especially when such industries may be in a difficult capital situation.

In general, labor organizations also react to automation and technological change with concern over how well society is preparing its members for it in terms of education and training. There is considerable emphasis on the need to prepare people for a lifetime of changing jobs and functions. For as society becomes increasingly affected by automation, the ability of the individual to adapt to the required changes will depend upon his ability to achieve a new mobility.

Implications for Education

The new technology will require a life of multiple careers to a degree far exceeding that of the past. The process will be accelerated at such a rate as to require a drastic re-thinking of the methods of education and training, so that the individual will acquire a more generalized and flexible preparation for a working life — a "mobility of mind." Industry and government will have to become increasingly interrelated in education and training matters. If the generations of today and those yet unborn are to survive in an automated society, they must not be subjected to archaic academic curricula and obsolete vocational education.

These are some of the general concerns of labor organizations when they view the new society of automation and technology. Many labor economists are extremely pessimistic when they analyze what has been accomplished along these lines in comparison with what remains to be done.

I do not share their dispair when the issue is the general ability of the total economy to successfully adjust to the automated society. There will not be unanimity of view in the processes applied to achieve this state, but I am confident that the size and diversity of the American economy will be sufficient to the task, with a healthy assist from the continuing emergence of an American ethic in social responsibility.

But while the larger problem may not be as insoluable as forecast by yesterday's prophets of doom, the very real concerns of individual employees may prove far more difficult to resolve under the present system of introducing technological change than is realized.

Gus Tyler, in his recent analysis of American trade unionism, *The Labor Revolution,* summarized the dichotomy between success in the total economy and failure to solve individual problems:

> "New jobs for other people elsewhere may produce a tranquilizing statistic for
> the sociologist. But those other jobs do not lessen the tragedy for the head of
> a family who has just lost — or feels he has lost — his whole future."[2]

The total economic growth which means more jobs does not protect any particular employee's job, and in fact, the machine operator whose job is eliminated by an automated machine rarely becomes the programmer who provides instruction for the new machine.

Consequently a whole pattern of responses has developed to protect specific jobs and individual income. However, most collective bargaining proposals by labor organizations have been *responses* in the nature of a defensive reaction. As such they can be classified as compensatory and are not characterized by the elements of initiative and innovation which one would expect from an industrial partner.

Automation and Collective Bargaining

In 1964 the International Brotherhood of Pulp, Sulphite and Paper Mill Workers, AFL-CIO compiled a representative sample of collective bargaining clauses that had been negotiated to ease the impact of automation. These were categorized and published in a study entitled, *Automation: Economic Implications and Impact Upon Collective Bargaining.*[3] A review of this study and later publications indicates that the basic methods of adjusting to technological change have not changed significantly since that time. The following is a general summary of the most frequently negotiated adjustment clauses:

Education and Training: Programs of educational advancement and retraining have been negotiated where employees learn new skills during regular working hours at company expense and without any loss in wages. Frequently the clauses specifically provide that an employee whose job has been changed or eliminated has the right to receive the necessary training without loss or reduction of pay to perform the skills demanded to run the new machinery which has been introduced.

Trade Union Security: When a new job classification is created after technological changes have been instituted, some agreement clauses provide that the new classification cannot be transferred to a non-bargaining unit status.

Relocation Allowances: Companies generally agree to provide financial assistance in the case of "involuntary" transfers of a permanent character requiring a geographic move.

Income Security Guarantees: These generally provide that an employee will not lose his job or suffer any reduction in wages as a result of new machinery, manufacturing techniques and processes, or technological improvements. These sometimes involve personalized or "red circle" wage rates with possible provisions for a share in future general increases.

Adjustment Allowances: When there are no guarantees against reduction in pay, the parties may agree to a clause which provides a supplemental wage for some period of time to help the employee adjust to a lower wage.

New Job Classifications and Wage Rates: Many agreements provide for consultation with the union and joint negotiation of all new classifications and rates. This is particularly important in the case where there are existing job evaluation or incentive payment plans and where the new technology creates a situation in which the employee no longer has control over his own rate of production.

Seniority and Preferential Transfers: Most agreements protect the long-service employee, his seniority rights, credits and transfer privileges over "new hires."

Attrition: A superior method of adjusting to job elimination because of technological change is to introduce the change at a rate consistent with a company's annual rate of retirement, deaths and voluntary quits.

Pension Vesting and Portability: Multiple careers are made more feasible through liberal vesting or portability clauses in pension agreements so that the employee can take advantage of possible job opportunities without losing his accrued pension rights.

Early Retirement Pensions: Through adequate benefit levels available at an earlier age, employees can leave the production cycle and begin useful lives as active citizens.

Shorter Work Week: Provisions for sabbaticals or extended vacations, for the gradual lengthening of paid leave periods for older workers, and for shorter workweeks throughout the year have been negotiated.

Supplemental Unemployment Benefits and Separation Pay: When terminations and/or layoffs become inevitable, clauses designed to cushion the impact of unemployment through direct cash payments can help provide assistance to complement the meager unemployment compensation benefits provided by the states.

Joint Committees, Advance Planning and Negotiation: There is a developing trend for companies to participate in joint manpower planning with unions to enable constant negotiations in implementing technological change.

This review of collective bargaining response to automation and technological change illustrates the defensive nature of labor organizations' reactions which were mentioned earlier.

However, it should be pointed out that collective bargaining has expanded in at least one respect to adjust to the new pressures. Areas which traditionally had been marked as management perogatives have now become the subject of normal discussion and negotiation. Moreover, new techniques and different mixes of old techniques are necessary to determine what provisions should apply to the new kinds of jobs created by new systems of production. Thus, there has been some progress, but not the degree one would have expected.

The "Innovative Lag"

The responsibility for this "innovative lag" must be shared equally by both management and labor. The primary cause for their mutual lack of creative ingenuity in dealing with the effects of automation and technology upon the individual employee has been their failure to implement the most basic principle which should govern the introduction of change.

Earlier there is mention of joint committees, advance planning and negotiation. It is this extremely important first step which almost universally has been inadequately performed. In some respects this may be the result of both parties being too aware of the adversary character of labor-management relations and too insensitive to areas of possible mutual cooperation. While the adversary element is a natural and proper aspect of the relationship the introduction of automation into a plant or industry affords the opportunity to expand another very natural and proper aspect − mutual cooperation.

When technological change is being considered, both parties can bring into the discussion differing considerations for final decision. Management will stress the *economic* aspects of technological change; labor will emphasize its *social* consequences; and the final process should be an adequate combination of the two disciplines.

We have begun to understand increasingly in recent years that the most effective method of analyzing problems is the multidisciplinary approach. Consequently, in approaching phenomena such as automation we should concern ourselves with the total impact of the innovation, and develop a proper mix of priorities in making our decisions.

Expansion of Cooperative Role

The expansion of the cooperative role in introducing technological change must include full participation by employees in the process of which they are a part. Imposed procedures of introducing change will not work. Those who are affected must participate in the decision making process.

This concept is not new to the American tradition; It is as old as indignation over the Stamp Act and "no taxation without representation," and as new as citizen participation in the planning processes of the present experimental Model Cities Program.

Indeed, the United States always has been a nation of participatory democracy in which the people involved have a major stake in determining their collective destiny. From the early town meetings to the growth of enfranchisement throughout our history this has been the case.

"Industrial Democracy" has not developed to the same degree, because of the dissimilarities involved. But corporations are creatures of the state, and as such, their decisions and decision-making processes are becoming increasingly challenged, whether they involve technological change, pollution, or the social consequences of their products.

The issue of introducing automation and technological change can afford a great opportunity in the evolution of modern industrial society. Through joint participatory decision-making we can affirm our traditional belief in the intrinsic value of the individual. Through enlightened cooperation we can fashion social forms which will have meaning because they respect the basic integrity of the individual. And, we will once again demonstrate that a free collective bargaining system is capable of the growth and development necessary to adapt to changing times and technologies.

REFERENCES
1. American Federation of Labor and Congress of Industrial Organizations, *Labor Looks At Automation,* Publication Number 21, (AFL-CIO Department of Research, Washington, 1966)
2. Gus Tyler, *The Labor Revolution,* (Viking Press, New York, N.Y., 1967) p. 84.
3. John P. Burke and John J. McNiff, *Automation, Economic Implications and Impact Upon Collective Bargaining,* (International Brotherhood of Pulp, Sulphite and Paper Mill Workers, U.S.A., 1964).

11

Educational Institutions in an Age of Technological Change

Frederick L. Bates

EDUCATIONAL INSTITUTIONS IN an urban industrial society occupy a critical position in the social structure and perform a vital set of functions. Schools and colleges must simultaneously: (1) prepare people for assuming and maintaining their places in society, (2) interpret the rapidly accelerating pace of change and development for the members of society, and (3) exert leadership in scientific, social and philosophical development in order to generate even greater adaptive change. The burden of these tasks becomes greater and greater as other social institutions, notably the family and the church, undergo change and falter in their contributions to the performance of these same functions.

Education in an age of technological revolution is the key to adaptation of people to society and of society to change. The very success of the technological revolution itself depends on education. Technological change breeds social and cultural change and social and cultural change necessitate resocialization or reeducation of the people who must carry out the revolution on the one hand and adapt it on the other.

Educational institutions today are ill-adapted in their structure and practices as well as in their philosophies to play their roles in the new technological revolution. Such institutions have one foot planted firmly in the past with the other in the future and a gap is widening, creating a painful wrenching of the educational groin. Nowhere is this more apparent than in the case of institutions of higher education. Colleges and universities are, through physical and biological research, continually generating technological change. Their focus in research and development is on the far distant future. With respect to the organization of colleges and universities for teaching and learning, their focus is on the past. They ask, "How can we recapture the sense of community and thus reestablish the meaningfulness of teacher-student relations?" How, in short, can we remain as we think we once were?

Education Technology

Educational organizations such as public schools, colleges and universities as well as vocational and technical schools employ an educational technology. All technologies may be defined as man-machine systems that employ an organizational structure into which tools and machines have been integrated. This is done in such a way as to facilitate the performance of a function or the production of some product by the people who form the organization. The technology of education lags far behind technological developments in other segments of society.

For the most part, the educational organization of our society employs the same technology that has been employed for the past one hundred years. The technology of instruction is that technology employed in the actual educational process. It is the man-machine system through which teaching and learning takes place. Today, as in the past, the central operating technology consists of the teacher who conducts a class that is held in a "self contained classroom" aided by such simple tools as blackboards, chalk, pencil, paper, books, desks and chairs. It is true that modern machinery is sometimes employed in this process. If so, it is a mechanized way of doing the same thing that has always been done. For example, mimeograph machines turn out exercises that are handed out to students where the students were once required to copy such material by hand. Slide projectors are used as substitutes for hand drawn charts and figures, or for material once presented by a more primitive means. Television is used to present lectures to students gathered in a classroom and serves as a substitute for a live teacher performance.

In short, the software (social organization) of schools remains the same and the hardware of modern technology is simply used as a substitute for cruder tools and techniques. The system of organization used in education was designed, or more properly, evolved in an earlier stage of development in society and was adapted to its levels of technological achievement and its rate of social change. It is the thesis of this discussion that educational systems and institutions must be reorganized if they are to: (1) adapt to the rate of social and technological change that is occurring, (2) play an adaptive role in assisting people in society to function in a situation dominated by change and, (3) take advantage of modern technology to play these roles in society.

Role of the Teacher

In order to meet the challenge of education in the future, the role of the teacher must change just as the role of the researcher, the engineer and the organizational manager have changed. In research, the day of the individual investigator working alone in an isolated laboratory is long since past. The Louis Pasteurs, Madame Curries and Charles Darwins are outdated models for scientific inquiry as are the Thomas Edisons and Henry Fords in engineering. It is not that their imagination and brilliance is outmoded, but it is the context within which they worked that is dated. Not one of these individuals is likely to have refused the opportunity to work in a modern laboratory and have at their disposal not only the hardware but the software of modern research. What science learned from them, it built upon and improved. Their discoveries and contributions to science cannot be attributed to the crudeness of their laboratories, a lack of financial support or to their lack of human assistants but to their imagination, perseverance and intelligence, even under rather trying circumstances. No one would advocate returning to these circumstances as a means of producing the results they obtained.

With respect to the technology of teaching, matters are quite different. It is almost as if Mr. Chips, or perhaps, Socrates, remains the model of the ideal educator. Universities that are forging ahead in the facilitation of research through innovation in both hardware and software are floundering and even taking longing glances at the past with respect to instruction. Professors and students alike view emphasis on research and on the changes it has created in the roles of the professor and student with alarm and distrust, and even advocate a moratorium on such activities or a turning back of the clock to an earlier stage.

The difficulty with our present institutions of higher education lies in the failure of instructional technology to keep pace with the change in the technology of research within universities and with technological change outside universities. While we have radically redefined the role of the professor as a researcher, we have failed to redefine his role as an instructor. By redefining the research role, we have created the so-called knowledge explosion and placed a heavier burden on the instructional technology. This has its greatest effect in universities where there is a dual responsibility for research and instruction. It has also placed a new and ill-understood burden on the Junior College and the Liberal Arts Institutions, where research is not a part of the organization's mission.

The effects of the technological revolution in research, both basic and applied, have been unequally distributed in institutions of higher education. This revolution has taken place largely in the sciences and in allied fields of engineering. To a lesser extent, it is now affecting the behavioral sciences. The Classics, Humanities and the Arts have been almost unaffected. As a consequence, on the same campus, there is a growing gulf between the science faculties who have tasted and promoted technological change and the more conservative non-science faculties who have been affected by it only indirectly. In the Arts and Humanities creative work and scholarship, which are the functional equivalent of research in the physical, biological and social sciences, are carried on using patterns that have changed little over the past century. It is these patterns of creative work and scholarship to which the classic role of the professor as instructor is adapted. It is with these patterns that maximum consistency is obtained between the role of the professor as teacher and his role as scholar or researcher. So long as the *modus operandi* of the scientist approximated that of the creative humanist, conflict between the scientist's role as researcher and teacher were minimum. This is not to imply that such conflict was nonexistent but rather that it was held within manageable bounds.

Change In Research Roles

Change in the technology of scientific research has forced a redefinition of the role of the scientist in research and has, thereby, resulted in conflict with the instructional roles. These changes can be summarized as follows: The scientist is now the planner and manager of a research organization or team that depends on complex and expensive systems of hardware and, in most cases, a complex network of human specialists who cooperate with him as colleagues or assist him as subordinates. Typically, the senior scientist spends his time as an executive or manager of an organization, seeking to finance the operation, to plan and coordinate it and to interpret its output to the supporters and consumers of his scientific output. Where once the scientist was the primary actor in the laboratory, executing the research process with his own hands and observing his data with his own senses; he is now either removed from these activities or fast approaching that point and becoming a manager of the research process. To be effective, he must not only be able to identify and define significant scientific problems and design a method for solving them — but he must be able to marshal the technological and human resources to carry out his plan, and be able to manage these resources in a complex process of human activity.

These activities are, to a large degree, incompatible with the traditional pattern of classroom teaching. They are a full time job; as demanding as operating a sizeable business enterprise and as complex as directing an academic department or college once was.

In research, the scientist has become the manager of a system of activities. He marshals and organizes resources and directs their application to problem-solving. He is not the executor but the manager of research. As a teacher, however, he is in a different position. He is the actor on the educational stage; the actual performer before the audience.

This educational role must change. Professors as teachers must redefine their roles so that they see themselves primarily as the manager of the learning process rather than the instructor in the classroom.

In order to redefine the role of the professor as instructor, it is necessary to recognize the true mission of institutions of higher learning. The university, as well as the college and junior college, exist to facilitate or, perhaps, to maximize learning in a human population. This mission is subdivided into three submissions: (1) The facilitation of learning by the faculty through research and scholarship so that new knowledge is continually created; (2) the facilitation of learning by students to whom the tested knowledge of the past as well as the new knowledge created through research is made available; and (3) the facilitation of learning by the general public through devices that disseminate knowledge beyond the narrow bounds of the campus.

It is not the mission of universities to teach, but rather to promote and facilitate learning. Learning implies both research on the part of faculty and learning on the part of students and the public. Teaching implies one method through which learning is facilitated. It is a method that defines a certain limited range of roles for the professor. These roles tie him to the educational technology of the past and make it difficult for him to take advantage of both the hardware and software of modern technology in the process of facilitating learning. The technology of teaching involves the teacher and his action before a group of students as the central element. The teacher's behavior in the form of lectures, discussions guided by judicious questions and comments, along with conferences and tutorial sessions, make up the central techniques of teaching. These behaviors may be augmented by the occasional use of audio visual aids. But these aids are tied to teaching as a process rather than to learning. Testing is used as a method of evaluating the amount of learning produced by the teaching process, but it is rarely used to evaluate teaching as an input into the learning of students. Tests evaluate students; they do not evaluate teachers.

Redefinition of Roles

So long as students, professors and the public regard the mission of universities and colleges, and for that matter public schools as that of teaching, the technology of education will remain "hung up" on the technology of the past. They will also continue to perceive a basic conflict between the research, instructional and public service missions of universities and colleges. If, instead, we could redefine the role of educational institutions to become that of maximizing learning, the technology could change and adapt to become more consistent with the technology of research and development. Given the maximization of learning, the point of view should follow that any technology that moves in this direction would be legitimate and desirable. The educator (public school teacher and college professor) would become a professional in the use of a diversity of means for accomplishing his objective. His new dominant role would be as the manager of the process whose objective is to increase learning. He would concentrate on diagnosing learning problems, identifying and testing methods for dealing with these problems, prescribing and supervising the applications of these methods and evaluating their effectiveness in producing the desired result. His problem would be to marshal resources and manage their application rather than to function as the central active ingredient in the process. As pointed out, this has already happened in scientific research activities and has yielded significant results. Instructional roles should now move in the same direction.

A number of ingredients, some of which employ modern technology should become involved in the learning process. For example, a given course of learning (not instruction), could employ a combination of the following:

1. Carefully prepared documentary type films or television tapes designed to convey information in a form that will facilitate learning.

2. Programmed instructional devices such as "teaching machines, computer simulations and games."

3. Field and laboratory observation.

4. Controlled discussion groups and question-answer sessions.

5. Tutorial consultations.

6. Reading assignments.

7. Lectures on the latest information and ideas not yet available in other forms.

8. Constant testing to evaluate the effectiveness of each input into the

learning process so that it can be altered, improved or abandoned where ineffective.

The educator, who is interested in maximizing learning, should seek a combination of inputs into the learning process that facilitate it. He should approach this process without having his imagination fettered by out-moded philosophies and organizations, and should be constantly willing to experiment with new combinations of ingredients.

Most of the experimentation that is now taking place with the newer technologies merely uses them as a substitute for older methods. For example, television instruction, as it is being used in the majority of cases, is used to convey a lecture by a professor or teacher to a larger audience. Such lectures can be polished and supported by considerable graphic materials, but they are still lectures. As such, they use an old fashioned method of "teaching" in conjunction with a modern communications media.

Examinations are now graded by machine. Grades are recorded and reported by computer techniques. The examinations and their uses remain the same. They are still used merely to rate students and to furnish feed-back to them on their results in such a way as to alter and improve these inputs.

Modern technology has the promise of providing new means of accom-plishing educational goals. This can only be done by employing technology in new and imaginative ways; not merely as a means of doing the same "old thing" to more people quicker and at a lower cost. It may prove true, as much evidence shows, that TV lectures are as effective as live lectures. The important point is that live lectures were never especially effective themselves. Thus, TV, unless used in a new and imaginative way can allow us to do a bad job quicker and in a larger volume − a goal that is not especially appealing.

There are two important problems of educational institutions upon which all others ultimately depend. Modern technology through creating rapid social change makes these problems more critical today than ever before, and offers a chance of solving these problems for the first time. The problems are:

1. Educational institutions must constantly survey their environment to determine what the requirements of a rapidly changing society are in

terms of the learning needs (research and education) of its people. With accelerating social change, these requirements change almost day by day. If educational institutions are as slow to respond as they have been historically, we are constantly educating people to live in a society that no longer exists. In the words of the youth of this generation, education becomes more and more "irrelevant." Instead of leading the society into the future, it is "dragged kicking and screaming" into each generation of change just a little too late to be of maximum value to its clients.

2. Educational institutions, on the basis of constantly updated information on the requirements of the society, must constantly examine its own internal technology and change it as well as the type of learning it produces to fit these new requirements.

Summary

Never in history have educational institutions faced a comparable challenge. Historically, societies have changed slowly. Educational institutions created organizational machinery for dealing with this slow rate of change. Careful, deliberate, ponderous processes have classically been employed to create educational adaptation. In the past, decades have been required to introduce new fields of study into institutions of higher education, and more decades for these fields to penetrate into the lower levels of the educational system. This was no great problem in a world that changed but little from decade to decade. Schools and colleges could educate a person for a lifetime. What he learned in school would lose little of its value or validity over the years. Now, between the freshman and senior year, change is so great that we may train a person for a life that no longer exists. This year, for example, a surplus of PhDs have developed. These people started graduate work three or four years ago in a world that appeared to have an inexhaustible capacity to absorb people with doctors degrees. Even now, it seems inconceivable that things could have changed so much.

More than anything else, educational institutions need continuous feedback from the environment that is immediate and accurate.

The research technologies of the social and behavioral sciences, combined with the communications and computer technologies, must be immediately applied to solving the problem of keeping in constant touch with the "learning market." We must develop an accurate, rapid and constantly functioning means of surveying the educational environment to determine what the situation is to which we must adapt. Routine survey research with computer backup must become a part of each educational organization's technology.

To employ the knowledge obtained from the environment, it will be necessary to create new organizational forms that allow rapid and adaptive response within educational organizations. The structures must loosen up so that innovation is favored and rewarded and the future, rather than the past, becomes the orienting focus of organizational policy. Unless educational institutions can change to meet the challenge of the technological revolution occurring around them, they will be responsible for creating further maladjustment between the various parts of our social system.

12

Toward a Global Economy

James C. Hetrick

ANY DISCUSSION OF the impact of automation on society must recognize two trends which are existent to the society, and must be expected to continue over at least the immediate planning horizon of ten to twenty years. These are: the population growth in virtually all parts of the world, with the rate of growth inversely proportional to the then standard of living of the group of society being considered; and a drive in all nations toward a rising standard of living, and enhanced consumption.

These two trends must also be considered in the context of an existing state in which man has already measurably affected the environment in which he lives. There is currently much concern in the United States and in other industrial states over the problems broadly described as pollution — pollution of the water and of the air, both chemical and thermal. We are faced with the problem of rectifying, at the cost of many billions of dollars, situations which should never have been allowed to arise. Currently, the cleaning up and control of the environment has become a national goal; and our news media, belatedly becoming aware of conditions which were accurately forecast by ecologists and conservationists long before the critical stage was approached, vie with each other in showering us with shock statistics and in the enthusiastic endorsement of spectacular, impractical, and misguided short term measures of relief that are certain to backfire.

Let me hasten to add that I regard the concern with pollution as necessary and belated, and deplore only the hysteria and lack of coordination with which the problem is being approached. Further, I fear that the panic reaction to an immediate crisis will cause us to overlook the basic problem of which pollution is only an immediate symptom.

Since the present is the future of the past and today is the first day of the future, we should learn from history in order to avoid worse disasters as our societies continue to develop as biological entities within a single precariously balanced ecosystem.

The basic first step in such planning and examination is an improved understanding of the interrelationship of technologies and their role in the satisfaction of needs and wants. To do this, we must develop a much better understanding of how the economy functions and interacts with technology. The United States today is presumably the overall most advanced economy on earth. Yet, it may be criticised as an economy which is based upon waste. It is this wastefulness in the economy which has led to many of the pollution problems which are of immediate concern. The failure to use manufactured durable goods such as automobiles, appliances, etc. over their entire useful economic lives and to design for longer lives has led to a waste and disposal problem of massive proportions. Failure to reclaim and recycle materials leads to the massive chemical and sewage pollution problems which we are encountering. Failure to use energy efficiently gives the massive air contamination problem existing today. Yet, such an apparently wasteful economy has led to, and seems to be necessary to, an overall very high energy consumption and a very high standard of living.

It comes as a constant surprise to travelers even in the more advanced western nations outside the United States, to find that, in absolute terms, the cost of manufactured goods exceeds the cost of similar goods in the United States, with very few exceptions. Somewhere there must be a mode of operation at which the waste which we incur and the economies of large-scale production which we now achieve artificially by that waste, must be at their balance point to obtain an optimum economy. Presumably by increasing and fully utilizing the economic life of manufactured articles, by increased efficiency in the use of materials and energy, and by the control of further improvements in technology, we could maintain a high level of per capita consumption while considerably lowering the level of work involvement by means other than increase in unemployment.

Assuming we have developed such models of technologies and economies, by the elaboration of known techniques, we should then face the problem of selecting and directing research and development programs to maintain and advance economies by novel means and the development of new industries. If the problem areas can be defined, the techniques of technological forecasting can be applied to such project definition. In this context, it should be noted specifically that technological forecasting must go beyond the purely material manipulative technology and include sociological implications. Jantsch has given an excellent four point summary:

1. Technological forecasting is an integral part of the planning process unfolding between the levels of policy, strategic, and tactical planning. At policy-planning level, the scope of technological forecasting is the clarification of scientific-technological elements determining the future boundary conditions of the planning environment; at strategic planning level, its scope is the recognition and comparative evaluation of alternative technological options, in other words, the preparation of the technological decision-agenda; and at tactical planning level its scope is the probabilistic assessment of future technology transfer. Technological forecasting is never a straight prediction.

2. Consideration of the future potential technology transfer is set in a broad economic, political, social, and anthropoligical context – in other words, technological forecasting is integrative forecasting.

3. Technological forecasting emphasized the assessment of effects (for example, technological capabilities, such as speed, temperature resistance strength, etc.) and of impacts, not the actual description of a technical realization (a machine or apparatus, etc.). This implies that technological forecasting – in accordance with full-scale planning – is most useful in an outcome-oriented framework, not in an input-oriented one.

4. Technological forecasting takes an essentially non-deterministic view, combining exploratory (opportunity-oriented) and normative (mission-oriented) thinking. This implies, inter alia,: The shift of emphasis from short- and medium-range tactical to long-range strategic and policy thinking; and the trend toward large-systems thinking, going beyond the industrial and economic systems to include the joint systems of which society and technology are the constituents.[1]

Since technological forecasting is not universally recognized and is still an emerging body of techniques, it might be well to add to Jantsch's four points the following observations of Prehoda:

T/F may be defined as "The description or prediction of a foreseeable invention, specific scientific refinement, or likely scientific discovery that promises to serve some useful function." These are functions that meet the requirements of industry, the military services, other government agencies, and the general needs of society.

T/F can be used to consider some of the consequences to industry, government, and society, if a technological capability is indeed exercised. In this regard, it can be integrated with other forecasting and long-range planning activities involved in economics, politics, and international relations.[2]

Fundamentally, T/F is based on an understanding of the current limitations of science, which have been defined accurately by Sir George Thomson:

"Technology is governed by scientific principles, some of which are understood, and there is accordingly a basis for prediction . . . developments which do not contradict known principles and which have an obvious utility will in fact be made, probably in the next hundred years. No doubt there will be discoveries which will transcend what now appear major impossibilities, but these are unpredictable, and so are the practical developments which will follow them."[3]

In addition to Sir George Thomson's principle requirement, several other key ingredients are part of the T/F process:

1. It must be recognized that some reasonably well-defined technological barrier has brought progress in a field of science (biological or physical) to the point of diminishing return — the top of the "S"-shaped curve characteristic of all technological development.

2. The "technical barrier" must have a relationship to a recognized need, perhaps one not understood by the general public.

3. There must be some advantage in bypassing the subject "technical barrier" — this could be a military of a non-weapons oriented requirement.

4. There must be at least some conceptual approaches which do NOT violate well-defined natural laws. These can involve techniques one or more orders of magnitude beyond current technology, including very radical departures from historic approaches to the basic barrier.

5. The ancillary supporting technology, instrumentation, measurement techniques, etc., must be available or capable of being developed to laboratory operational status, within a reasonable time period.

6. There must be agreement among responsible members of the scientific community that the conceptual approaches fall within these broad guidelines, and these technical reviewers must have the courage to make favorable recommendations when the respective segments of the "technological forecasting jigsaw puzzle" fall into place.

7. Government officials, who influence and control R&D funding, must be capable of recognizing the significance of technological advances made possible by Hahn-Strassmann point breakthroughs, and be willing to fight for adequately supported programs.[3]

In context of this discussion, and if we are to assume oxygen to be found to be the first limiting resource, in the application of technological forecasting the prime objective would obviously be research towards means of generating energy economically which do not involve fossil fuels or otherwise interfere with the carbon dioxide-oxygen cycle involved in photosynthesis. The techniques should enable us to describe in rather straightforward fashion those areas in which we should be most interested.

Assuming then that the problem of energy procurement without atmospheric pollution or depletion is solved, some other resource would in turn become first limiting on an ever expanding population base or on a fixed population base with an increased standard of living. Statistics on per capita usage of various materials in advanced versus underdeveloped countries could be produced ad nauseum. Future process development will minimize wastage and emphasize the need to recover and recycle materials, not only to minimize pollution, but to recover precious and irreplaceable atoms. However, it is clear that new materials or alternative sources for existing materials must be found, and that the model building and fore-casting techniques could be used to define the problem and to indicate the direction in which to look for the solution.

We should note that the problems of energy and the problems of materials are not independent, since the development of cheap power from any source would revolutionize the extraction of metals from ores which are now not economical to process. Very large masses of material can be handled in order to extract small quantities of lighter elements if the energy for the processing is fairly cheap. Further, new mining techniques, especially those of deep mining, will become increasingly dependent on inexpensive power coming from relatively transportable devices.

The picture drawn thus far then becomes one in which we can foresee great changes in the economy, with new industries emerging and estab-lished industries dwindling or changing in nature. We must then aim to understand clearly the effect — which is presently debatable — of automa-tion on employment. At the moment, it is possible to find experts on the subject who will argue vehemently on either side of this question, but the truth is that the facts are by no means clear. Certainly it is true that automation has not brought about massive unemployment in the U.S. or Western Europe, where the societies are most highly automated.

Another aspect of the effect of automation on employment, has been the debate about the increase in leisure brought about by mechanization and automation. Such statistics as may be quoted are generally given in the form of hours per work week, or unemployment statistics, or both. It can be debated whether such figures represent an increase in leisure, or a redistribution of leisure. Detailed statistics are not available over a long time span, but such statistics as are available may be misleading because of the expansion of the workforce as a percentage of the total population, changes in work week varying in different industries, and the very nature by which unemployment statistics are developed as people enter and leave the workforce. Thus Prehoda (op.cit., pages 36-37) bases his argument on the increase in unemployment in the post-recession periods from 1948 through 1961. However, a common inflator of unemployment statistics in recession years arises from the fact that when a man becomes unemployed, frequently his previously nonworking wife will seek employment. If she finds it, the total workforce is unchanged, but the unemployed workforce has risen by one. If she does not find work, the total workforce employed has decreased by one and the total workforce unemployed has increased by two.

A more meaningful measure of leisure would be found from a statistic which would show variation, if any, in man hours worked per capita. Such a statistic seems not to be directly available, but an index can be derived from the gross national product per capita in constant dollars, and the output per man hour relative to 1958, developed and published by the Bureau of Labor Statistics. These two quantities are shown in the table following for the years 1960 and 1967, which was overall a period of full employment, with a constantly expanding economy, and a period during which the drive towards automation was intense:

	1960	1967	Ratio 1967/1960
1. GNP/capita* (1958 dollars)	2,699	3,361	1.245
2. Output per man-hour* (1958 = 100)	105.0	132.0	1.257
3. Index of man-hours/capita (1) ÷ (2)	25.7	25.5	0.992

*Source: Statistical Abstract of the United States, 1968.

It will be seen that during this period the output per man hour increased by somewhat more than 25 percent — an amount sufficient to lead to a lowering of the work week by a full day per week, or to lead to a 20 percent rate of unemployment. However, during the same period the gross national product per capita rose by almost the same amount, 24.5 percent. The ratio of GNP per capita to output per man hour, which represents an index of man hours worked per capita, decreased by only 0.8 percent during this period. It could thus be argued that increases in productivity were either matched by increases in consumption directly, or were indirectly absorbed by shifting the worker to the production of other goods. There could obviously have been very little increase in leisure. In fact, considering the growing sprawl in urban areas during this period, and the increased difficulties of commuting, it is probable that overall a decrease in leisure occurred.

However, it seems to be true, and necessarily so, that automation has brought about and will increasingly bring about, the need for training and retraining people as jobs disappear and new jobs appear. It is my belief that in the relatively near future business will accept the social consequences of automation in a formal fashion and look upon the cost of retraining and relocating persons displaced by automation as part of cost of installing new products and new processes. Such a cost when made formal will simply appear as another cost to be considered in the evaluation of new investment opportunities.

In addition to the retraining of workers technologically displaced, we must learn to retrain managers to solve the future problems created by technology. A current best seller is "The Peter Principle," the theme of which is that in an organization an individual will rise to his own level of incompetence. Unfortunately, like Parkinson's, there is a considerable amount of truth in the Peter Principle which may arise as a consequence of automation and the advance of technology in general.

There exists in the literature of management science an algorithm known as "the assignment problem," which is used, among other things, for the allocation of manpower to jobs. If we consider a given number of jobs available, and a given number of individuals to fill the jobs, and assign an index of proficiency indicating the relative value of each individual in each job, the assignment algorithm can be used to find the optimal solution, that is, the solution in which the total sum of job competence is maximized. If now we make two assumptions:

(1) That the total pool of competence in an organization is less than the total pool of competence required as measured in some quantized fashion, and
(2) That the index of competence for different individuals on various jobs is approximately rank-correlated,

Then we find that the optimal assignment results in precisely the condition described by the Peter Principle. That is, the maximization of competence may be looked on as the minimization of incompetence, which is the best that can be achieved when there is an insufficient existing total pool of competence.

However, managerial competence depends on two factors — the ability of the individual and his training for the situation which he encounters. If management learns from history, from experience and from the past, the new situation will find him relatively incompetent and the learning process must be accomplished on the job. As technology advances in greater steps, the gap between experience needed and experience available, must necessarily increase. To close this gap, it will be necessary to look ahead, to anticipate the problems of management before they arise, to develop techniques for the solution of these problems, and to train the appropriate managerial personnel in the use of these techniques before the need to apply them arises.

REFERENCES

1. Jantsch, Eric, *Technological Forecasting in Perspective.* Paris: OECD, 1967.
2. Prehoda, Robert W., *Designing the Future.* Philadelphia: Chilton Co., 1967.
3. Thomson, Sir George, *The Foreseeable Future.* New York: Harper and Rowe, 1960.
4. Gabor, Dennis, *Inventing the Future.* New York: Alfred A. Knopf, 1964.
5. Gordon, Theodore J., *The Future.* New York: St. Martin's Press, 1965.
6. Bell, Daniel (ed), *Toward the Year 2000.* Boston: Houghton Mifflin Co. 1968.
7. McHale, John, *The Future of the Future.* New York: George Braziller, 1969.
8. Clarke, Arthur C., *Profile of the Future.* New York: Harper and Rowe, 1962.
9. Ferkiss, Victor C., *Technological Man.* New York: George Braziller, 1969.
10. Wells, Ashton & Taylor (eds), *Technological Forecasting and Corporate Strategy.* Bradford University Press, 1969.

13

Automation: Government's Role and Responsibility

John E. Mock

THE WORD AUTOMATION first entered the English language in 1946, and yet the concept is old — nearly as old as civilization itself. We are told by historians that even before the Revolutionary War, Oliver Evans put into operation near Philadelphia a fully automated, waterpowered, flour mill. And centuries before, the historian of antiquity, Xenophon, wrote that in Persia "there are places even where one man earns a living by only stitching shoes, another by cutting them out, while there is another who performs none of these operations but only assembles the parts." Although this was not automation in its truest sense, yet it did foreshadow by many centuries Adam Smith's innovative concept of division of labor. In fact, Xenophon expounded upon the fact that "he who devotes himself to a very specialized line of work is bound to do it in the very best possible manner."

Automation, as we know it today, is a synthesis of four important historical developments: mechanization, continuous process, automatic control, and rationalization.

Mechanization was the process by which man created machines to relieve himself of heavy work or to manufacture items of greater quality at reduced cost. Mechanization, which led to the industrial revolution of the eighteenth century, is often denigrated by philosophers as a process which wrenched mankind from a halcyon, pastoral existence and dumped it unceremoniously into the smelly, soot laden, dreary manufacturing towns of the 18th century England. Yet in actuality it released the majority of mankind from the slavery of serfdom and provided a degree of economic and social independence possessed previously only by members of the ruling classes.

The concept of mass production, was known and was occasionally applied (as in flour mills) in the 18th century. It was Henry Ford and his

European counterparts who seized upon the mass production concept to improve the productivity of labor, speedup the manufacturing process, and reduce total production costs. Although production line work tended to alienate workers because of its tedious and demanding nature, yet it provided an abundance of low-cost goods such as the world has never before known.

The third essential principle of automation, automatic control was applied to windmills in the 17th century to keep them facing into the wind, and to steam engine in 1788 by Watt, who invented the flyball governors to automatically control engine speed. However, it was not until World War II that breakthroughs by Wiener in control theory, and by defense industries in electronics, permitted the development of sophisticated feedback controls. The process of automatic control has given man such precision in manufacturing processes and in guidance systems that for the first time man has been able to leave his eco-sphere earth and travel to another body in the solar system. Man's conquest of space, exemplified by footsteps on the moon, is mute testimony to the power and versatility of modern technology (and especially the process of automatic control). (The garbage left behind on the moon may, on the other hand, symbolize the ambivalence inherent in any technological achievement i.e., each new technology inevitably brings with it certain undesirable consequences — often unpredicted, and perhaps inherently unpredictable — which must then be treated in an improvisatory manner.)

The final concept of automation, rationalization, is the application of reason to the solution of problems. This is the basic principle that unites the essentially engineering aspects of automation to the economic, political, and social aspects through the managerial process. Rationalization is as simple as the concept of applying digital-computer control to the operation of entire oil refineries, and yet as complex as the belief that man can apply the essential concepts of automation — through the process of systems analysis — to solve such vital problems as urban blight and environmental pollution.

Thus, from the viewpoint of historical perspective we are able to see how the four elements of automation have coalesced to form one of the most powerful techniques ever developed by mankind. And the story is far from being finished. We are still in the Stone Age of Automation barely perceiving, through a glass, darkly, visions of the opportunities lying ahead in the Bronze Age of Automation.

The Political Problem

To the average person, it is natural to consider automation as falling within the industrial sphere, and with a little stretch of the imagination, even in the broader social milieu. But the application of automation to the political process may seem incongruous, if not actually improper.

Let us start by considering the simple problem inherent in a democratic form of government — determining the will of the people. In the days of the Greek city states it may have been feasible to assemble all citizens to discuss and vote on pertinent issues. But as political units grew larger, this simplicity was lost, and the democratic process became a representative process. Representatives, being human, have no way of knowing what the will of their constituency is on each and every issue. In addition the representatives are subjected on occasion to rather strong (and usually competing) political pressures. Thus, many have yearned for the simpler days of yore and to the New England "townhall" concept of democracy, considering such a system as being inherently more representative and less corrupting.

Modern technology now offers the possibility of applying automation to the political process so that each citizen can vote directly and immediately on each issue, giving an immediate read-out of each decision. Thus we can imagine one hour each week being set aside on all TV channels for our government officials to present issues for decision. By hooking up a simple signal generator to each home telephone, all votes would be fed into a high-speed computer to provide a real-time read out — instant automated democracy.

But is this really what we desire? Can the average citizen really become sufficiently well informed on a wide variety of issues to vote intelligently? Will he be willing to devote the necessary time and energy to the political process? In a sense we have returned to the centuries-old question as to whether a representative should merely reflect the opinion of his constituency or should reflect his own considered judgment. The latter view has nowhere been expressed more clearly and movingly than in the formulation of Edmund Burke, made nearly two centuries ago in a speech to his constituents in the city of Bristol:

"Their (the voters') wishes ought to have great weight with him (their representative); their opinion high respect; their business unremitted attention. It is his duty to sacrifice his repose, his pleasures his satisfactions, to theirs, and above all, ever, and in all cases, to prefer their interest to his own. But, his unbiased opinion, his mature judgment, his enlightened conscience, he ought not to sacrifice to you, to any man, or to any set of living men. These he does not derive from your pleasures; no, nor from the law and the Constitution. They are a trust from Providence, for the abuse of which he is deeply answerable. Your representative owes you, not his industry only, but his judgment, and he betrays, instead of serving you, if he sacrifices it to your opinion ... Government and legislation are matters of reason and judgment and not of inclination; and what sort of reason is that, in which the determination precedes the discussion, in which one set of men deliberate, and another decide; and where those who form the conclusion are perhaps three hundred miles distant from those who hear the arguments? ...

"Parliament is not a congress of ambassadors from different and hostile interest; which interests each must maintain, as an agent, and advocate, against other agents and advocates, but Parliament is a deliberative assembly of one nation, with an interest, that of the whole; where, not local purposes, not local prejudices, ought to guide, but the general good, resulting from the general reason of the whole. You choose a member indeed; but when you have chosen him, he is not a member of Bristol, but he is a member of Parliament. If the local constituent should have an interest, or should form a hasty opinion, evidently opposite to the real good of the rest of the community, the members for that place ought to be as far as any other from any endeavor to give it effect."

Perhaps we can say that, if nothing else, automation may force us to re-think many of our basic political concepts.

Let us now consider some of our most critical societal problems and the relationship of automation to them. We are all familiar with the triad of problems: (1) population explosion — typefied by the fact that our current 200-million population will increase to 300-million by the year 2000; (2) population implosion — exemplified by the continuing rush from rural to urban communities, putting increasing pressure on already overburdened and archaic urban institutions and finally, (3) population displosion — in which we find a polarization of our metropolitan areas, with the more affluent moving to the suburbs, leaving behind the lower income groups with a depleted tax base. If ever a set of problems cried for a solution, this is the set. Automation played a role in creating these problems, for example, (by releasing many farm workers from rural employment); does it offer any near-term solutions to help ameliorate these problems?

There is good reason to believe that automation can provide the governmental decision-maker with improved methods for tackling complex urban problems. One line of development of high current interest is Professor Jay Forrester's (MIT) concept of Urban Dynamics. Forrester has developed in detail a dynamic model of the processes that affect the life and decay of cities. These models, which permit dynamic experiments on digital computers, should be more realistic and relevant than the familiar scale models of city planners. They will offer governmental decision-makers an extremely valuable tool for perception of present trends and for prediction of future likelihoods.

Forrester's work, to-date, with his automated urban model indicates that present tax policies and legal structure within the cities are largely responsible for the urban decay so visible throughout America. Forrester shows that past efforts to prevent or eradicate urban blight have produced little success, and policies for reviving urban areas have failed because such complex systems, unlike simple ones, defy solutions suggested by human reason and intuition. Simple systems tend to be linear and involve only one feedback loop, whereas complex systems are nonlinear and involve multiple feedback loops. In simple systems cause and effect are closely related in time and space, whereas in complex systems they are often so far apart as to obscure completely their relationship.

Thus quite often we find that intuitive measure proposed for short-term urban improvement are counter-productive and often are detrimental in the long run. One of the striking conclusions Forrester reaches is that "underemployed-training programs and low-cost housing programs, although they seem promising, may actually hasten degeneration, while demolishing slum housing and replacing it with industry to create jobs — a policy that is widely frowned upon as inhumane — tend to set in motion a number of desirable long-term trends."

Such automated models accompanied by demonstration programs are possibly the decision-maker's only hope to gain the vision and understanding needed to ultimately solve our complex urban problems.

These then are a few of the more significant problems associated with automation. Let us now see how government is attempting to deal with these problems.

Drucker emphasizes the point that each organization has an important and distinct role to play in society, and that society is served best when each organization concentrates its efforts to satisfy that role. In general, then, we would expect business to do best by concentrating on bringing automation into the economic realm, social institutions on bringing automation and technology into the social sphere, and governmental institutions on introducing new techniques into the political system. Up to a certain point this simplistic point of view is adequate, however, it fails under the following circumstances: (1) In some areas an overlap of responsibility will exist where no one institution has primacy, (2) in some areas, all institutions may deny having any responsibility, and (3) in some areas institutions with primary responsibility will fail to absorb all the diseconomies resulting from their actions. Therefore, in certain cases, government will be forced to step in and play a role for which it is not ideally suited but which it must assume because of a failure to act properly on the part of some other institution.

Having played a role in state and federal governments over the past quarter of a century, I would like to discuss primarily the responsibilities of government in the introduction and management of automation. Rather than attempting to be comprehensive in my remarks, let me focus attention primarily on the problems which have already been outlined.

The Micro-Economics Problem

The ultimate responsibility lies with government to see that workers displaced by automation are able to find suitable employment elsewhere. This in no way relieves labor and management of their primary responsibilities in this area, but it does point up the large residual interest the federal and state governments have in maintaining full employment and in preventing undue economic hardship to any citizen. This governmental responsibility can be partially satisfied by providing education and training courses to better qualify workers for a broad-spectrum of job opportunities; by operating effective job information and job placement services and by promoting sound fiscal and monetary policies conducive to full employment and to an expanding economy. As long as the economy is healthy and growing, the impact of job elimination on the individual is minimized.

What the government should not try to do is to discourage the introduction or application of new automation devices. It is abundantly clear that any region or nation which fails to keep up with the application of modern technology, soon finds itself unable to compete in the national or world markets, thus leading to a slow but steady decline in the regional economy.

The Macro-Economics Problem

On the macro-economic scale, government has the responsibility of seeing that all its citizens have a reasonable opportunity of participating in a thriving economy. On the national level, this means that the federal government must be in a position to provide information and to guide its citizens and industries into those new fields of technology promising greatest future growth. This may be accomplished through tax incentive schemes (to prevent obsolescence of current industries) and through technology forecasting methods to make sure that industry has the necessary information and encouragement to move into new areas as they become ripe for exploitation.

At the regional, state and local level, it is necessary for each level of government to take measures to keep the area progressing along with the nation as a whole. As an example of policies and programs which can be initiated by such governments, let me cite some recent actions taken by the State of Georgia.

Although Georgia's per capita income has risen steadily over the past several decades, it continues to lag the U.S. average by approximately $600. This can be attributed primarily to the preponderance of low technology industries and the lack of automated, high technology industries in Georgia. To improve this situation, the Georgia Science and Technology Commission has launched a major effort to create or attract automated, high technology industry.

One of the first major efforts of the Commission was the establishment of the Ocean Science Center of the Atlantic in Savannah, Georgia to serve as a nucleus for the development of oceanographic industry. Several million dollars of state and local funds have been used to create an oceanographic center for industry and a university research facility (as part of the University System of Georgia). This total facility will increase income in the coastal plains region, will provide higher level employment for technicians in the Savannah area, and will help keep those graduates of Georgia colleges, interested in oceanography, in the Savannah area to work in the field of marine resources and coastal zone management. Thus, not only will this move into oceanography act as an economic accelerator, but it will also serve to reduce the "brain drain" problem which is so critical in the South.

Another program initiated by the Commission is designed to develop a major biotechnology industrial center in Georgia. A third program is aimed at developing a Georgia transportation research center. Such State-spawned institutions will act as economic stimuli and will help in solving critical problems, e.g., problems of health care, transportation, and urban mass transit.

In addition to such specific actions, the State is attempting to build up the general scientific and technological base of the State through technology innovation and technology transfer programs. A Georgia Inventor's Exposition has been created to bring together inventors, innovators, investors, manufacturers, and distributors with the ultimate goal of stimulating innovation in Georgia. The Commission is also working on establishing a regional patent search center in Atlanta, which would serve as an agent of technology stimulation. In addition, the Commission has launched a detailed study to identify those factors which have been important in stimulating the development of high technology industry in such areas as Boston (with its fabulous route 128 complex) and Menlo Park. Factors which have been tentatively identified as being significant are:

1. The technical knowledge which makes new technology possible.
2. A community climate which is receptive to innovation, change, and growth.
3. A political and governmental structure which encourages new technology.
4. Availability of necessary labor and management skills.
5. A sufficient supply of risk-taking entrepreneurs.
6. Availability of venture capital.
7. Effective distribution and marketing.
8. Good schools, climate, and recreational facilities.

By identifying the significant factors, we hope to be able to create the necessary environment to spawn or bring high technology industry (complete with automation) to Georgia.

The Education Problem

It is obviously one of government's prime responsibilities to provide adequate education for its constituents. Education is a changing concept — it is becoming simultaneously more intensive and more extensive in nature. As we enter the "knowledge society" of the future, education may play a continuing role throughout the lifetime of an individual.

The key educational problem facing all levels of government today is how to automate the educational process — reducing total costs while at the same time increasing effectiveness and efficiency.

At the moment, in spite of all the claims made by proponents of teaching machines, computerized education, etc., technology has had absolutely no effect on our total education system. As Dr. A.G. Oettinger of Harvard has recently pointed out: "Local rhetoric about educational goals and possible new technologies is sharply at variance with the reality of schools. Before we allow ourselves to be dazzled by new technology, let us note that the single most common technological tool of education, the book, which is also the most ancient, has been and still is being misused. Libraries are impregnable citadels; use by students is constrained because it might wear out the books, get them out of proper shelf position, or lead the students away from the lesson plan. Why should we expect more from more 'exciting' technological innovations?"

In spite of the fact that new technological developments — teaching machines computerized instruction, system analysis — have not yet had a major impact on the educational process certainly does not mean that they are worthless. In fact, they are essentially our only new hope for increasing the efficiency of education and for bringing costs under control.

The Health Problem

One of the aspirations of our citizens is to have adequate health care at reasonable cost. The goal is a rather elusive one in that costs continue to mount while the shortage of health care personnel continues to grow. As with education, automated health care systems must be developed to improve the efficiency of the total health care process Such a comprehensive health-care system must include preventative measures as well as diagnostic and curative techniques. Some progress is already being made in the use of multi-phasic screening techniques, and in computerizing certain standardized routines in a few leading hospitals. But this is merely a beginning. The federal government must continue to fund heavily the development of health care technology and automated systems — the state governments must concentrate on training additional health care personnel and seeing to it that adequate health care is made available to all citizens .

As an example of action which State governments can take, Georgia has recently:

1. Established the Health Careers Council of Georgia, an organization to conduct an active recruiting program for more professional and technical workers in health-related fields.

2. Established through Georgia Tech a Health Systems Research Center to develop and apply new knowledge with respect to the design, experimentation, evaluation, implementation, and demonstration of new and improved systems for delivery of health services to the public.

3. Established the Georgia Institute for Development in Biotechnology to coordinate existing biotechnology resources and to initiate and stimulate new resources, especially in the business sector.

It is hoped that the combined results of such efforts will ultimately lead to a more efficient automated health care system.

Future Trends

The problems of automation highlighted in this discussion are current problems, currently being attacked by governments (at all levels) in conjunction with industry, labor, and universities. The problems, though extremely complex, will ultimately be resolved to the satisfaction of society.

As technology and automation work their way around the world — from the advanced to the underdeveloped nations — the rising expectations of the poor will be met and exceeded by an abundance of riches produced by our constantly growing industrial capabilities.

At the same time, man will turn his attention to using technology and automation in the social and political spheres. We currently see the first faltering steps being taken in developing automated models of community growth and decay, of transportation networks, of medical and hospital practices, and of crime and criminal justice systems. There is every reason to believe that these early applications of technology to societal problems will be just as effective as has the application of automation to industrial problems. If man is able to master himself, and avoid the early demise of mankind (through massive nuclear exchanges, through destruction of the world's eco-system by pollutants or through self-poisoning by pesticides, carbon monoxide, and hydrocarbon emissions), then he can look forward to a Golden Age in which his material wants will be satisfied and his innate, creative talents can be fully utilized. Aristotle once said: "When looms weave by themselves man's slavery will end." We are now nearing that point in time.

REFERENCES

Books

1. Bagrit, Sir Leon, *The Age of Automation*, New York, The New American Library, 1965.
2. Buckingham, Walter, *Automation*, New York, The New American Library, 1961.
3. Burck, Gilbert, *The Computer Age and Its Potential for Management*. New York, Harper & Row, 1965.
4. Butz, Otto, *Of Man and Politics*, New York, Holt, Rinehard, and Winston, 1962.
5. Carter, Launor, *Personalizing Instruction in Mass Education by Innovations in the Teaching-Learning Process*, Santa Monica, California, System Development Corporation, Report No. SP-2722, January 27, 1967.
6. De Dimone, Daniel V., *Education for Innovation*, New York, Pergamon Press, 1968.
7. Drucker, Peter F., *The Age of Discontinuity*, New York Harper & Row, 1969.
8. Forrester, Jay W., *Urban Dynamics*, Cambridge, Massachusetts. The M.I.T. Press, 1969.
9. Gardner, John W., *No Easy Victories*, New York, Harper & Row, 1968.
10. Kahn, Herman Wiener, A.J., *The Year 2000*, New York, The Macmillan Company, 1967.
11. Martin, E. Wainright, *Electronic Data Processing*, Homewood, Illinois, Richard D. Irwin, Incorporated, 1965.
12. McLuhan, Marshall, *The Medium Is The Message*, New York, Bantam Books, 1967.
13. Morse, Philip M., *Operations Research for Public Systems*, Cambridge Massachusetts, The M.I.T. Press, 1967.
14. Nelson, R.R., Peck, M.J., and Kalackek, E.D., *Technology, Economic Growth, and Public Policy*, Washington, D.C., The Brookings Institution, 1967.
15. Oettinger, Anthony G., *Run, Computer Run*, Cambridge, Massachusetts, Harvard University Press, 1969.
16. Regan, Michael D., *Science and the Federal Patron*, New York, Oxford University Press, 1969.
17. Schon, Donald A., *Technology and Change*, New York, Dell Publishing Company, 1967.
18. Scrag, Peter, *Village School Downtown: Politics and Education – A Boston Report*, Boston, Beacon Press, 1967.
19. Scott, Ellis L., and Bolz, Roger W., *Automation and Society*, Athens, Georgia The Center for the Study of Automation and Society, 1969.
20. Wiener, Norbert, *Cybernetics*, Cambridge, Massachusetts, The M.I.T. Press, 1965.

Periodicals

21. Allison, David, "Measuring the Good and the Bad of New Technology." *Innovation*, No. 9, 1970, pp. 44-54.
22. Brooks, Harvey, and Bowers, R., "The Assessment of Technology," *Scientific American*, Vol. 222, No. 2, February 1970, pp. 13-21.

23. Carter, Luther J., "Technology Assessment: NAE Report Explores the Methodology, *Science,* Vol. 166, No. 3907, 14 November 1969, pp. 848-852.

24. "Educational Technology in Higher Education: The Promises and Limitations of ITV and CAI," *Engineering Education,* January 1970, p. 384.

25. "For Technology Assessment," *Science News,* Vol. 96, September 6, 1969, p. 177.

26. Mendell, Jay S., "Technological Forecasting: The State of the Art," *The Futurist* December 1969, pp. 160-161.

27. "Regional Development Possible Despite National/Regional Conflict," *Industrial Research,* December 1969, p. 87.

28. Spector, Bertram, "Why a Systems Analysis of Technical Education," *Annals of New York Academy of Sciences,* Vol. 136, Art. 24, October 12, 1967, pp. 757 764.

29. Steele, Theodore K., "Operational Considerations," *Annals of New York Academy of Sciences,* Vol. 136, October 12, 1967, pp. 765-774.

30. "The Productivity Problem," *Technology Review,* Edited at M.I.T., October/ November, 1969, pp. 102-103.

31. Wolfe, Dael, "Assessing Technology," *Science,* Vol. 166, No. 3908 21 November 1969.

Reports

32. *A Study of Technology Assessment,* Report of the Committee on Public Engineering Policy, National Academy of Engineering, Washington, D.C., July, 1969.

33. *Knowledge Into Action: Improving the Nation's Use of the Social Sciences* Report of the Special Commission on the Social Sciences of the National Science Board, National Science Foundation, Washington, D.C., 1969.

34. *Technology: Processes of Assessment and Choice,* National Academy of Science Report, Washington, D.C., 1969.

35. *Telecommunications for Enhanced Metropolitan Function and Form,* Report of the Committee on Telecommunications, National Academy of Engineering, Washington, D.C., 1969.

36. *The Engineer and the City,* National Academy of Engineering Report, Washington, D.C., 1969.

37. *The Future South and Higher Education,* Southern Regional Education Board, Atlanta, Georgia, 1968.

38. *The Impact of Science and Technology on Regional Economic Development,* National Academy of Sciences Report No. 1731, Washington, D.C., 1969.

39. *Toward the Year 2000: Work in Progress,* Daedalus Journal of the American Academy of Arts and Sciences, Cambridge, Massachusetts, 1967.

14

Automation and Labor

Ben B. Seligman

BACK IN 1963 George Meany declared to the A.F.L.-C.I.O. convention automation is ". . . rapidly becoming a curse to this society" . . . He was not being merely truculent. His attack reflected a state of panic among many union officials over what they considered to be the job-displacing impact of automation. They were deeply concerned, despite their public commitment to technological advance. Mr. Meany was addressing himself to the government to take heed that a social problem was in the making: he knew better than most that collective bargaining had been able to deal with automation in but piecemeal fashion. The solution has since been achieved: tax cuts, special programs, inflation, and Vietnam. The character of these measures would be a subject for a long debate; however, let me address more specifically the issue of responsibility. That wage standards built by collective bargaining could be threatened, and that such workers as might be displaced would eventually look upon the union movement as a protective institution for those with jobs against those with none seems quite evident.

Areas of Concern

It was an uncomfortable situation for the unions. Despite a gain in factory jobs of about a million from 1961 to 1964, the fact remained that over the long haul the number of production workers in manufacturing had declined. There seemed little question to union men that automation could cut into the ranks of those workers who make up the bulk of their membership. Furthermore, the shift of the workforce to white-collar and service occupations posed additional problems for the unions for the patent fact was that they had not yet learned how to organize such workers effectively. The white-collar worker had an ingrained reluctance to join a union, believing himself superior to the blue-collar man. Supporting this attitude was a sense of identification with management. At any rate, management was evidently more successful in fostering such sentiments among white-collar people. Often the white-collar worker believed that individual effort was the key to achievement, and he was supported in this belief by his education, advertising, and the popular literature.

While academic analysts and corporate executives insisted that the effect of automation on jobs was no different from that of ordinary technology, the unions remained unconvinced. The greatest pressure from automation was in manufacturing, mining, and transportation, areas of traditional union strength. While, for the moment, the service trades seemed immune, it was small wonder union chiefs were disturbed. Yet for all the inventiveness in bargaining, which was described in some circles as "creative," the various devices left much to be desired. Adjustments to enforced erosion of the workforce through technology were limited to advance notice (to give the worker a chance to find something else); attrition (which closed down jobs after retirement or quits); early retirement (necessitating more funds in pension reserves to make it meaningful); severance pay (generally used to pay off accumulated debts); and other arrangements like retraining, automation funds and human relations committees. The cumulative weight on the bargaining process was enormous: In fact, collective bargaining as we had come to know it in the United States was not designed to handle all the problems stemming from automation. Therefore the "solutions" sooner or later evolved as gimmicks that failed to supply meaningful answers.

Furthermore, automation threatened to dissolve the one weapon available to a union – the right to strike. This was especially evident in the oil industry, where production in struck plants continued uninterruptedly despite the picket lines outside the gates. In 1961 the Oil Chemical and Atomic Workers' Union took out all the production and maintenance workers at the Gulf Oil Corporation's Port Arthur Texas, plant. Yet, manned by only 600 supervisory and technical personnel, the refinery turned out gasoline, fuel oil, and other products at 65 percent of the prestrike pace. After seventy-two days, the union caved in: Its search for "job security" for its members had failed, and all it could obtain was a promise of sixty-day advance warnings of layoffs. As if to drive home the nail, the company also won flexibility in making job assignments. The stike in an automated industry seems to be obsolete and the unions are able to worry only about protecting the jobs that are left. Or they can insist on "buy-outs" to compensate for those jobs that have become outmoded.

Many Automation Concerns

The struggle over the issue of automation was often manifested not only in bargaining but through arbitration and grievances as well. Illustrating the problem was the case of an automated drilling machine installed in an auto plant. The task of programming the machine had been assigned to engineers not in the bargaining unit. The U.A.W., however protested that the work now done by the tape had once been performed by toolmakers and therefore the programming job belonged in the unit. The arbitrator agreed, holding that the toolmakers had a vested right to the work. Management was chagrined that anyone should believe that a contract created a property right to a job. They strongly objected to the principle that work done by employees in a bargaining unit prior to the installation of automated equipment should stay in the unit after automation And the courts were remanding disputes to arbitration, rather than trying to settle these questions themselves. Yet the fact was that beyond questions of defining the scope of a bargaining unit most collective-bargaining agreements could not deal with automation problems: If a skill had been completely eliminated there was not much the union could do, unless special arrangements had been provided in advance.

It had been suggested by some observers that unions affected by automation should be merged, as perhaps ought to have been the case with the flight engineers and airline pilots. Although some mergers have been carried out, they have not always been simple matters, for not only has it been necessary to distribute officials' posts, but promotion and seniority lists and work rules have had to be merged as well. When specialized skills were involved, the problem became exacerbated, as the downgrading enforced by a new process was apt to be resisted with some bitterness. In several instances the prospect for certain organizations was a future of "ghost unionism," top-heavy with officialdom, well financed, but reduced in size and national influence. They came close to representing an entrenched but dwindling minority and appeared to be cut off from — if not at odds — with the poorer strata of the working class. Affluent shells of their former selves, they resembled the United Mine Workers, once a major social force in American life but now with little influence beyond the confines of the coal fields.

Perhaps the alternative might be some sort of amalgamation cutting across industrial lines, just as in the Thirties the C.I.O. cut across craft lines. As Dr. Margaret Chandler of the University of Illinois has said, unionism now needs to be organized around a process, in a kind of super-union covering a complete industrial flow, a complete technology. This kind of organization would be a natural response to management threats to move elsewhere or to subcontract some of the work: The superunion could overcome such whip-sawing tactics by organizing all the inside and outside workers in an industry.

Still, serious organizing problems would remain. Although automation shrinks plant employment, organizing cost for the unions do not drop proportionately. The Oil, Chemical and Atomic Workers" Union states that it costs as much to organize 100 men as 500 men. And as the units are smaller with automation, the union must spend more on servicing and enforcing contracts than do other unions of comparable size. For example, whereas the Rubber Workers' Union has about 350 contracts to negotiate and service, O.C.A.W. must handle 1,600 different agreements. The amalgamated structure with company-wide agreements would do much to ameliorate the problem.

Defensive Measures Predominate

For the present, most of the affected unions could think only of work rules as a protective device. They were only a defensive measure, resulting all too often in charges of "featherbedding." As technological change was introduced, management was often able to play one group of workers against another. In one such instance, cited by George Strauss, the company announced its intention to lay off some workers and then proceeded to grant pay increases to a few senior workers in excess of what the union had asked for the new jobs. The maneuver effectively split the workers and turned them against the union. Maintenance work is often subcontracted, generating marked hostility, as employees see their own jobs given to others while the union is unable to protect them.

Such problems are quite important for the central issue in collective bargaining is job security, and all the measures employed to meet automation's challenge are directed toward that single objective. So-called "automation funds, "progress-sharing" schemes, extended-seniority work rules supplementary unemployment benefits, sabbaticals, shorter hours, and human-relations committees are all intended to provide protection for workers. The unions insist that a property right does inhere in a job and that if that right is destroyed it entails some quid pro quo. Granted that the high road to total security for the worker lies in full employment even that condition of bliss would not fully assuage his sense of unease. Some companies expand, but other decline; technology wrenches traditional occupational patterns out of shape; and certain areas experience losses in jobs while others gain. From the union point of view the struggle to achieve security is ever present.

Although workers may be aware that adjustment to automation can be made through attrition or retraining, much of their immediate concern is rooted in a fear of changed job content and work rules. If the same amount of work is to be done by fewer men, what will be the nature of the individual jobs? If some jobs are less risky than others who gets what work? As the work force dimishes how are seniority lists to be handled; Furthermore, can attrition operate quickly enough over time to reduce the work force to levels management says are optimum, or will outright firings have to be utilized?

It has been suggested that early retirement would help cut down the workforce. Workers have an enormous interest in all the private pension schemes that have burgeoned since World War II: More than twenty-two million employees are involved, and the assets of these systems total more than $70 billion. Yet in an automated economy some workers may not stay on jobs long enough to earn pension rights. They may have to move from job to job, even from one industry to another to find employment The solution to this problem ought not be too difficult — let the pension credits follow the worker. That is, pension rights ought to be as portable as savings accounts. The banks and insurance companies could easily develop the requisite mechanisms.

But early retirement — how shall it be paid for? About $13,300 is required at age sixty-five to give a man a pension of $100 a month. If he retires five years earlier, the benefit is cut to $66 a month, and there is no Federal social security to supplement his retirement income at that age. If early retirement is to be meaningful, the benefit would have to be increased or the gap "bridged" with an adjustment at the time social security does take effect. But to provide a $250-a-month benefit at age fifty-five, with a social-security adjustment ten years later, requires a reserve of about $35,000. The contributions would have to run about 40 to 50 cents an hour, compared to the present 10 to 15 cents an hour. One wonders if there are many companies around prepared to undertake such a cost.

New Instruments Needed

Some firms are seemingly generous. The Humble Oil Company offered the mariners in its tanker fleet an early-retirement program under which a seaman with fifteen years of service could retire at fifty years of age. This offer was part of a plan to reduce crews by 16 percent in order to minimize the effects of installing automated deck-maintenance and tank-cleaning equipment. For every early retirement said the company, one less employee would have to be laid off. At age sixty-five, a retired employee was to receive 96.4 percent of full benefits; at age fifty-five a retiree would have 72 percent of what he would be entitled to if he could work another ten years.

And what of automation funds, once quite the rage. After studying their functioning in the coal-mining, longshore, meat-packing, garment, and musical-entertainment industries, Thomas Kennedy concludes that such funds have ". . . provided little or nothing in the way of benefits for the workers displaced by automation." None of the funds adequately protected the accumulated rights of those displaced, nor did they provide the assistance that might have been necessary to tide them over to new jobs. Nor could the funds be used effectively for retraining because of restrictions arising from state unemployment-insurance laws. As Kennedy remarks, automation is often a way of meeting a competitive situation, it is unlikely that firms seeking to automate would be willing to assume an added burden unless required to do so. At best, an automation fund may provide some share of the savings for the workers who remain. Furthermore, when the financing of such a fund is based on so much per hour of work, management has an inducement to automate in order to reduce its contribution per unit of output. Of course the unions are easily attracted to these schemes because they promise benefits to members in the future, but in the general excitement of creating a new instrumentality, the over all benefit program is all too often a public-relations device, according to Kennedy. The most controversial item on the agenda of adjustment is the shorter work week. Opponents argue that not only would it increase costs of production, no change in hourly rates, but also that geographic and occupational effects are more rigid than shorter work week advocates presuppose. Furthermore, the relationship between men and machines in many industries is said to be rigid, posing difficult technical problems in additional workers. The response, however, seems obvious: If enough men were reabsorbed, industry could readily resort to multiple work shifts. The warning continues, however: A shorter workweek might seriously affect productivity; and the work pace would be intensified with harmful effects.

The key issue at this point, and the one most difficult to establish, is the relationship between the length of the workweek and output. The workweek will vary from industry to industry and even from one location in the same industry, depending on weather, raw materials availability, state of mind of the worker, or the irascibility of the foreman. Presumably, hours per week can be longer, the shorter the total work period. On the basis of such rough and inelegant concepts, corporate executives will argue a thirty-eight hour week is optimum, a "calculation" generally ridiculed by labor. The latter insists that shorter hours reduce absenteeism and accidents — and enhance total output. But, say opponents, it is a presumption that the length of the workweek that maximizes profit is longer than workers are willing to put in. If the typical marginal analysis is modified, optimum point for the length of the day from the firm's point of view defined by the intersection of marginal hourly cost and marginal hourly revenue. It is likely, however, that the supply curve for labor at any given hourly cost will begin to bend backward prior to the optimum point resulting in a smaller profit for the firm. The solution to such a dilemma, it is suggested, is to reconcile workers' and employers' work weeks by applying "human engineering" to convince employees to put in more time, or perhaps to increase their wants through advertising and salesmanship so that they will work for more discretionary income.

Arguments for Shorter Hours

We may note that from 1860 to 1960, average weekly hours dropped from sixty-eight to forty-one, or about fifteen minutes a year. The sharpest decreases occurred between 1900 and 1920, with New Deal legisltation during the Thirties cutting the work still more. Total work time, however, has not declined so sharply, owing in all probability to the larger number of part-timers and the greater number of holidays, expanded vacations, and the like. Labor Department data indicate that 90 percent of the workers in manufacturing are on a forty-hour schedule. Although shorter schedules in manufacturing are uncommon, the proportion of workers in major metropolitan areas who work shorter schedules increased from 6 percent to 10 percent between 1953 and 1962. Short schedules are widespread in the printing and women's apparel industries, retailing, construction and offices. It is evident that the short workweek is not unknown in American industry.

Arguments at the turn of the century favoring shorter hours were based on considerations of health, the need to diminish fatigue, accidents, and the like. Employers insisted on the cold logic of economic science: As wage rates were set by marginal productivity, any increase in rates occasioned by shorter hours would be inflationary unless the countervailing forces of high productivity were to prevail. Furthermore, such higher costs would induce a substitution of capita for labor. Although it is difficult to establish the precise relationship, it is nevertheless clear that, historically, reduced hours have not depressed productivity: In fact, they may have enhanced it. Could it be that the point of optimum marginal productivity never had been attained? But, of course, this esoteric concept is simply a technical term for labor demand and is a much more complex element than the concatenation of marginal outputs and costs makes it seem. The consequence is that rules of thumb are apt to be the guiding principle in decision making: On this score, the worker's thumb does not differ appreciably from the employer's, and if he deems the shorter work-week to be a desirable goal he has his reasons.

A Transitional Scheme

One might consider transitional scheme, as was once suggested by the United Auto Workers. This scheme would maintain the forty-hour week whenever unemployment was less than a specified percentage of the labor force; a reduction would occur only when unemployment went above the indicated ratio. The procedure would be reversed as soon as unemployment declined. The funds necessary to maintain take-home pay as the work week was reduced would be supplied by a special "adjustment fund" accumulated through a modest payroll tax. In effect, the fund would operate as a stabilizing device. Unfortunately, there was little public discussion of this striking idea. Yet, clearly, manipulation of weekly hours is one of the devices that can be used to deal with automation impact.

The A.F.L.-C.I.O. estimated that a million new employees would be needed to provide the same number of work hours should one hour be cut from full-time work. A reduction to 37-1/2 hours would require 2.7 million added workers. Of course, there are limitations to these gross estimates, and union economists acknowledge them. A uniform reduction in all industries might not be feasible, part-time workers would have to be brought up to the new hours specifications, and geographic and skill factors might impose constraints.

Often with automation there is dissension among unions. As jobs are abolished, occupations realigned, and task mechanized, a scramble ensues to see which union will exercise jurisdiction. Clearly the union most affected by technology is apt to be the loser, as in the case of the Flight Engineers' International Association, which cannot even take consolation in the sort of survival enjoyed by the Journeymen Horseshoers (290 members employed at race tracks) and the Cigar Makers (4,700 members making speciality smoking items).

When jets came to the airline industry, fewer pilots were required. Seeking to protect its members' jobs, the Airline Pilots' Association decided to seize jurisdiction of the engineer's seat in the cockpit. In 1957, A.L.P.A. tried to have the F.E.I.A. charter revoked by the A.F.L.-C.I.O.; failing, it then decided that the third man ought to be a pilot also and sought to appropriate the seat through bargaining. Despite F.E.I.A. strikes the A.L.P.A. eventually won out.

Another case history is that of the printers, whose history of craftsman-ship goes back almost half a millennium. Their struggle for job security and the effort to deal with technology's impact have been long, beginning with Mergenthaler's linotype machine in the 1880s. Yet the frustration of the newer labor organizations would be compounded if they were to look to the printing trades for solutions. One of their answers was reproduction, or "bogus work," a form of nonwork that the printer disliked intensely as an insult to his pride of craft and that was traded off sooner or later for another coffee break. Still when newspaper publishers can look to the composing rooms of the future that will automatically compose copy from the typewriter to the finished page without human hands, the printer has ample cause to worry. Although the union's attempt to control the work process has been bitterly attacked as featherbedding, the choice has been between that and no work. In the absence of work the featherbed is preferred. The worker can always look to the management featherbed and management make-work to provide a model. The preference for softness is a two-sided affair.

Can Solutions be Found?

The inability to achieve an effective solution culminates in work stop-pages, often of long duration, as in the New York newspaper strikes of 1962-1963 and 1965. One result of the settlement in the first dispute was the formation of a joint board, modeled after the human relations com-mittee in the steel industry, which at least began joint discussions of job security, efficiency, and the impact of technology. The newspapers agreed to share some of the savings from automation — in this instance, the use of tape for setting financial tables — by paying something into a special union fund. The problem of job displacement by machines was by no means solved. however. After the strike both the New York Times and Daily News installed high-speed machines to cast metal sterotype plates for their rotary presses. The reduction in the number of jobs ranged from 15 to 20 percent. And the various newspaper unions appeared to have become reconciled to the reduction in the number of available jobs. The important thing was how many openings would be available in the future and the amounts of the payoffs to those displaced.

When negotiations for a new contract opened between the typographers and the New York newspaper publishers in late 1964, none of the crucial problems had been solved. The employers agreed that automation was the central issue: There was need to increase productivity. The union was prepared to accede to computerized typesetting, provided there was "mutual advantage." Quite simply, they meant controls on the rate of introducing automated equipment and a share of the savings achieved from new machines. In addition, the union was willing to accept early retirement, provided that it was properly financed − and they insisted that it could be. From the union's standpoint this plan seemed the only way to provide an attrition guarantee to those presently employed. The publishers, on the other hand, insisted on complete freedom to mechanize, an attitude the union has described as "hopeless."

It seems evident that the only answer to automation through collective bargaining is to take care of those who are inside the plant: Little can be done for the worker already shunted aside and even less for the younger worker who wants to get in. Let me illustrate the problem with one more case history.

Case of the Railroads

On the railroads automation has loosened the desperate holding action of the Unions. Once among the country's most powerful the Railroad Brotherhoods are caving in before technology and politics. In 1959 the railroad companies wanted to lay off all firemen working on diesel locomotives in freight and yard service and insisted on an unrestricted right to set crew sizes. This right would have meant the abolition of almost 60,000 jobs. The five on-train operating unions immediately threatened to strike if the work-rules changes were carried out, for they insisted that, not only was train safety involved, but also firemen's posts were needed to provide training for future engineers. The companies screamed "featherbedding" in full-page newspaper ads throughout the land. Few listened to the plaints of the workers or their unions.

In October 1960 a presidential railroad commission was created, which produced several immense volumes of statistics that sounded the death kneel of the firemen. The fifteen-man tripartite body held hearings, listened to experts of all sorts, and in ninety-six days produced 15,000 pages of transcript and 20,000 pages of exhibits. It studied the pay structure on the railroads employment trends, age distribution of the workers, retirement rates, and unemployment benefits and examined experiences in other industries. The commission then concluded that "a gap had developed between technology in the industry and the work compensation rules" — that is, that there were too many workers around and that the railroads were right in trying to get rid of them. The few who might remain were to be rewarded with a 2 percent wage increase.

Needless to say, the unions rejected the commission's proposals. An emergency board under the Railway Labor Act then proposed retraining special allowances for redundant workers, and arbitration of displacements disputed by the union. The operators were ready, but the unions once again stalled: They were biding their time to hit the railroads the only way they knew how — with the strike. But, as usual, President Kennedy under stood full well what was in their minds, and, armed with the Council of Economic Advisers' prediction that six million workers would be out of jobs one month after a rail strike and that the ensuing depression would endanger the national security, he asked the Congress in July 1963 to forbid railroad strikes for two years and to compel the operators and the Brotherhoods to keep talking to each other. Congress, however went further and imposed compulsory arbitration — which the President accepted. It was one of the few bills that moved over the Hill to the White House that year with more than deliberate speed. On November 26, the arbitration panel established by the statute ruled that up to 90 percent of the contested fireman positions could be eliminated — a crushing blow to labor that few noticed in the agony of the President's death.

When the Supreme Court refused to question the constitutionality of compulsory arbitration, another nail was driven into the automated coffin carrying the Brotherhoods to their doom. The railroad operators immediately announced the layoffs: Fifteen thousand jobs were to be eliminated before the arbitration law expired in January 1966. But the operators moved with almost indecent eagerness: By April 1965 about 15,700 firemen, 42 percent of the total, had been removed from freight and yard service, and more than 6000 jobs were scheduled for elimination in 1966. The one saving grace was that a fireman with ten years' seniority might receive up to $8,000 in severance pay if he chose to leave. Even the industry conceded that more than 10 percent of those laid off were still without work by mid-1965. The union contended, however, that the figure was higher than that — closer to 30 percent. But a key point was missed in the discussion; most of the unemployed may have been absorbed sooner or later, but when they did find jobs these were generally lower in the occupational ladder and brought a lower rate of pay. This has been a common experience, typified most strikingly in the case of the miners and the packinghouse workers. At any rate, the operators could offer the consolation of unemployment insurance at $51 at week.

The unions — particularly the Railroad Trainmen — decided that they might just as well go for wage boosts rather than for job security, as the latter was down the drain anyway. They tried road-by-road negotiations in a campaign to split the operators' solid bargaining front. The operators refused unless work rules changes were part of the agenda. The unions made vague threats of a strike, driving the operators to court for injunctions. Nothing had been settled in all the jockeying, however, except that there would be fewer jobs for railroad workers. It never occurred to the unions that an effective consolidation of their efforts and perhaps of their organizations might help them achieve a better position vis-a-vis the operators. They might strike here and there, as against the Chicago and North Western in August 1962 and the Florida East Coast in January 1963, but to no much avail. Despite the "settlement" announced by President Johnson in April 1964, the situation remained an uneasy one. Some jobs were given up by the unions, whereas management agreed to more holidays and a few wage increases. The President temporarily had solved the bargaining impasse with a bit of characteristic arm-twisting.

By mid-1965 it was patent that the Brotherhood of Locomotive Firemen and Enginemen, almost a century old and once boasting 120,000 members, was expiring. It had fought for five years against the railroad companies' demand to wipe out jobs, and it had lost the battle. Few new firemen were now hired: The union had lost members as well as income, the latter at the rate of $360,000 a year. The "full crew" laws that once protected railroad jobs in some fourteen states were being repealed at a rapid clip, so that the arbitration ruling could be applied there as well. Meanwhile, the Engineers' Union, repeating what the Airline Pilots had done, deciding that "there's no sense fighting a lost cause to save the firemen." Indeed, the Engineers appeared to be trying to quicken the Firemens' end by raiding them for the few members who might have kept their jobs.

Efforts in the Steel Industry

Perhaps more effective solutions are those developed in the steel industry. The Kaiser Fontana plan, for example, may offer a partial answer. In March 1963, the union and the Kaiser Steel Corporation, a maverick among manufacturers, agreed to "share the progress" at the latter's plant in Fontana, California. The scheme included a guarantee that no worker would lose his job − at least for one year − because a machine had taken his place. If no other job were available, he was to go into a reserve pool and was assured of his income even if placed in a lower rated position. Furthermore, all the workers were to share in any cost savings achieved through greater efficiency. Such savings might come from anything that helped reduce the cost of steel − elimination of waste, working harder, or finding a new way to turn a dial on the control panel itself. During the first year, workers submitted more than 900 cost-cutting ideas, 80 percent of which were good enough to be adopted. The share going to the workers is 32.5 percent, a formula derived from the proportion of labor costs to total costs. The scheme is plant-wide, so that everyone can help make the pie bigger. In the first year the monthly bonuses averaged about $65 per man. In August 1965 the employees' share was 45 cents per hour worked, the distribution, however, amounted to 17 cents an hour, as the balance had to be placed in a reserve to pay for future increases in wages and fringe benefits. That is, the worker paid for his own benefits to come. And with each dollar of the bonus, Kaiser saved two. The company was hardly playing philanthropist. The workers began to think of the company's money as if it were their own. Cable lengths used by overhead cranes, which used to be junked when they snapped, bolts were horded as a housewife saves twine.

Yet the plan is still a "buy-out:" It has neither halted the advance of automation in the Fontana plant nor controlled its pace. An automatic scarfer, a machine that burns blemishes off unfinished steel, replaced not only the workers who used to do the job with oxyancetylene torches but also the cranemen, hookers, and inspectors as well. The displaced went into the labor reserve pool: At one time there were several dozen men in the pool awaiting reassignment; fortunately, they had been reabsorbed by the end of the year. Although the bonus has gone as high as 66 cents an hour, for the last seven months of the plan's initial year it dropped steadily until in May 1964, it hit only $14 for each of the 5,000 workers participating in it. As a result, enthusiasm for the scheme declined sharply: The incentive workers who used to average $50 to $60 a month in bonuses above their base pay were particularly bitter.

Part of the reason for the drop was apparently the company's installation of certain cost-cutting operations outside the plant, displacing work formerly done inside, and as the sharing applied only to Fontana, the workers lost out. They charged the company with chiseling. Kaiser, on the other hand, countered that raw-materials prices had gone up and that improved fringe benefits — the cost of which was charged to the saving fund — ate into the amounts the men otherwise might have received. In addition, the company felt that the union ought to have relaxed its stubborn grip on Section 2B, the work-rules clause.

The fact is that the Fontana plant has been able to operate at full capacity with 1,400 fewer workers than it had used a few years before. Kaiser believes that the normal 8 percent turnover in its workforce will keep down the number of bodies accumulating in the reserve pool. As a key problem in automation is not so much the one fired, although that is troublesome enough, but the one not hired, the Kaiser plan, interesting as it is, offers no answer to the question raised by the 1.5 million young people who enter the job market each year. Can the social effects of automation indeed be handled via the ritual of collective bargaining?

By urging an expansion of manpower retraining and relocation aid, the A.F.L.-C.I.O. itself acknowledges that the burden of automation is too great for collective bargaining. The particular approaches of individual unions are at best holding actions and at worst helpless rhetoric. The U.A.W. wants to compel management to respect the dignity of the worker and urge its locals to resist the erosion of its bargaining units. Although the Machinists' Union recognizes that automation poses problems, all it can think of is another conference or perhaps better severance pay. The I.U.E., the Rubber Workers, the Retail Clerks, and several other unions asked for joint study committees, but there was no answer from the corporations. The Mine, Mill and Smelter Workers and the Railroad unions, too, call for higher wages to be paid whenever new equipment is to be installed, a response sure to be used as an excuse to bring in more machines. The Butchers' want a year's notice on plant closing, transfers for the displaced, more separation pay, and a shorter work week. The fact is that the unions have no answer to the predicament posed by the new technology.

Thus the problem of automation requires a response that transcends the limits of collective bargaining. Essentially, this means that responsibility must be exercised on tripartite base — business, labor, and government — and solutions must be joint ones. If adjustment to automation can be facilitated by high levels of aggregate demand, then that is an approach that must be channeled through appropriate governmental devices. If the consequences of automation require that a downgraded work force be retrained, then that is a task that the three parties must confront. If the strictures imposed by new technology tend to shorten the ladder of opportunity, it will take the cooperative efforts of all three to add new rungs to that ladder. In essence, automation is a social process and the contemporary response must also be social.

15

The Automation
Environment

K. Robert Hahn

THE PRECEDING AUTHORS have reported on past and present attitudes and responsibilities related to the management of automation. I would like to cover three specific areas of today's Automation Environment:

1. The critical challenges and threats to business growth.

2. Development of the organization and management needed to respond to change.

3. Corporate development of job oriented schools.

As our market oriented economy hesitantly steps forth into the decade of the 70's, it is confronted with a flood of regulators and a tide of consumerism in a wave of ecological concern. From a businessman's point of view, we are engulfed in critical threats and challenges. We are all keenly aware of the many pressure groups that are lobbying for new legislation and the pending bills in Congress proposing a proliferation of regulations that would have a marked impact on business growth.

In the area of product safety, national commissions, consumer associations, and government regulators are now surveying, investigating, and recommending new legislation and regulations in most areas of consumer products. The name of the game is "let the seller beware," and as one harassed executive recently put it, we are in an era of the "phenomenon of rising expectations" where consumers' hopes outrun the best efforts of the design, development, and production of industry.

We find that we are a frustrated generation living in a permissive establishment with few restraints on irresponsible, sensational criticism. We are in an era where there is a great deal of criticism of large corporations for bigness per se. This attitude even pervades the Justice Department which has threatened to block mergers between the top 200 corporations.[1]

How Much Regimentation?

As a result of this environment and these trends, businessmen must face the fact that even the unthinkable can no longer be ruled out and that people outside the industry with their so-called objective point of view are writing the regulations for the new game. Consumer and industrial products will be charged with new standards of reliability and responsibility. The consumer protection movement will reach into new areas of pricing, pollution, noise, insurance rates, credit cards, and maintenance.

We have become the most powerful and productive nation in the world based on a market-oriented economy. Any historian of U.S. business or worldwide business enterprise is concerned with the present increase in regulatory devices that are restructuring our domestic and international economies and that will continue to limit the ability of businessmen to plan for the development and growth of their products. The primary issue facing our market economy is how much regimentation can business take in order to solve the public and social problems of the future.

As our market economy sputters into the 70's, we are under a cloud of inflation, high labor rates, and diminishing productivity. As we pass through a trillion-dollar gross national product in 1970, we do have high hopes for the future. However, there is great concern as we consolidate the gains of the 60's. There are many controls, restraints, and pressures from the government sector which will determine the ability of our so-called free market economy to function effectively. With over 100 federal agencies regulating in some measure most of our private economic activity, we do have cause for concern. One has only to see a proliferation of the regulations reported in the Federal Register to wonder where this can lead. In the 33 years since its inception, this publication of proposed rules and orders has grown from 3,140 to 20,460 pages per year.

In the concern for justice and fairness in the promulgation of new regulations, we have reached the point where quasi judicial proceedings have taken ten years to resolve ... and this can best be described as a *paralysis* of justice. Many litigants are now in a position of hoping *not for justice,* but *just any decision.*

A Chaotic Patchwork

What is the answer? Perhaps one approach is to develop greater participation in establishing national priorities and guidelines with the leadership of the administrative agencies. Each independent agency has become a prisoner of the system. As the late President Kennedy said in 1962, "A chaotic patchwork of inconsistent and often obsolete legislation and regulation has evolved from a history of specific actions addressed to specific problems of specific industries at specific times. This patchwork does not reflect either the dramatic changes in technology of the past half century or the parallel changes in the structure of competition."

We have literally thousands of Civil Service employees under the direction of 100 independent agencies, bureaus, and departments, each striving to carry out policies it believes are in the best interests of the public sector it serves and subject to all of the pressures of political, business, labor, and other special interests.

Climate In World Markets

U.S. business competes in world markets and we are exhorted by Secretary of Commerce Maurice H. Stans to reach $50 billion in exports by 1973.[2] Yet, government agencies and departments concerned with tariffs, trade agreements, foreign investments and loans, treasury rules, and IRS decisions are *not in concert* with the requirements for a competitive American business system in world markets. Who should speak out for U.S. policies to insure a favorable balance of payments?

The recent testimony before Congress on the 1969 tax reform bill clearly showed the misunderstanding of our national goals and aims when on the altar of inflation we sacrificed the business investment credit and made no other allowances to stimulate business investment.

The general approach to corporate tax policy in our country has been limited primarily to the domestic scene without the foresight to recognize our competitive role in world markets or what other governments are doing to encourage their business organizations to penetrate those markets. For example:

1. The United States has the smallest and most restrictive tax allowances for investment in productive facilities of any of the industrial nations.

2. The United States has the lowest ratio of capital investment to GNP of any leading industrial nation.

3. The United States has the highest percentage of over-age, obsolescent production facilities of any of the leading industrial nations.[3]

Our posture on recovery of capital equipment investment is the poorest of all the major free nations we compete with in world markets. Our guidelines for depreciation are always subject to negotiation with IRS and have beeen *as stable as a yoyo* for business planning purposes.

Unfortunately, businessmen have done a poor job in presenting to congressmen and administrators the economics of capital investment and capital recovery allowances and therefore weren't prepared to meet the thrust of the 1969 Tax Reform Act which was anti-investment.

We all realize that investment creates jobs and over 1-1/2 million new workers are coming into the private industry market each year. With a greater percentage of jobs in the service sector, which is less susceptible to productivity improvements, we should be encouraging automation equipment investment as the best tool to fight inflation. Only by making the productive process more efficient can we hope to improve the trend in cost of labor per unit of output. The past eight months have reflected no productivity gain in GNP.[4]

Due to the rapid inflationary increases, all businesses are confronted with a new threat — underdepreciation from inflation. Today's dollar at the present rate of inflation will be worth 50 cents in 12 years. To encourage investments in new business ventures and modernized equipment, our tax policies must protect the real capital of the business and tax only the profits. Therefore, a company must recover each year the number of current dollars that are equal to the year's capital consumption in the original investment dollars. This year, based on current depreciation rules, American business will pay income tax on $10 billion of capital consumption.[5]

It is interesting to note that since World War II American businessmen have invested the equivalent funds to generate over $200 billion in GNP overseas. Unless we correct the tax inequities on capital investment, encourage venture capital to develop new technologies and productive processes, and re-examine our tariff, non-tariff, and export-control laws, we will not be competitive with other nations for private capital investment.

Unfortunately, the full impact of a poor capital investment environment is not immediately ascertainable but its long-term effects are devastating. We have only to observe the historical economic cycles of our European nations to profit by their experience in this regard. Do we have

the wit to comprehend that the major reason for the tremendous annual
growth rate of the Japanese economy — which is over three times that of
the U.S. in the past decade — is primarily due to the favorable climate for
business investments encouraged and supported by the Japanese government?[6] The current apathy of businessmen, and the adverse attitude of
our government leaders to the need for a high level of productive investment, will dampen our economic ability to compete in world markets and
place the U.S. in a continuing trend toward unfavorable trade balances.
The cure for that performance is most drastic, as we have all witnessed in
recent years in Europe.

The Automation Environment

At this point I would like to present one management viewpoint on
how the organization will respond in the environment of the seventies.

What is the role of the multi-product corporation in today's automation
environment? What kind of organizational structure does it take to allow
business leaders to manage diversification more effectively? The one
common attribute of most of these companies is their ability to provide
the most effective utilization of resources in relation to current economic
requirements. This is done by establishing priorities for investment and
demanding that new programs as well as old ones be subject to constant
critical review. Corporate resources are then directed to those products,
markets, and profit centers which have the best opportunity for long-term
growth.

Organizations

The search for purpose, strategy, tactics, and goals for any business is a
very challenging one, and to the extent that these objectives are good for
business, perhaps they are equally applicable to government agencies and
administrative bodies as well as to non-profit institutions in the academic
and charitable world.

Participative planning in any organization is one way to approach the
problem. In order for all levels to understand their objectives and goals, it
is necessary to start from the very top with a statement of purpose,
strategy, and goals of the organization, and then each organizational level
below must do the same within the context of the overall purpose. It is
important that inputs from all the decision makers at all organizational

levels be included in determining the objectives and strategy of the organization, and the manner in which this is done is a measure of the effective
leadership of that organization. All concerned then understand the full
responsibility they have of measuring up to the performance of the goals
and objectives established.

Directions within any company and within any political, economic, or
social organization are constantly changing. Change insures an impact on
products and markets as well as on social and institutional objectives. What
to strive for, what to stop, and what to redirect requires priorities and
employment of criteria for review to either commence or discontinue a
project. We find that good judgment is based on values that are arrived at
in reasonable alternatives, and all concerned with the decision making
process should be committed to these alternatives as well as the logical
direction in which the organization decides to proceed.

A responsive corporate organization for a highly diversified company
requires delegation of action and decision making power to the profit
centers. Responding to new opportunities, new technologies and new
markets enables the profit-center manager to take the best advantage of
product life cycles and provides the incentives for his team to plan, risk,
and innovate and be rewarded accordingly.

Lear Siegler is a multi-national, multi-market, and multi-product company with 56 profit centers operating in 29 states and 16 foreign countries. The technologies we employ range from critical Apollo instruments to
automotive stampings and musical instruments. How will we respond to
tomorrow's environment? How will we achieve integration of our aims at
all levels of the organization with minimum restraints on our managers?

The following ideas are presented as aids in this endeavor:

1. There must be a clear understanding of corporate goals and objectives by
all organizational levels involved in profit making decisions.

2. The corporate purpose, goals, and strategies must be clearly written and
explained in participative management meetings and communicated to key
personnel within each profit center.

3. Through participative planning sessions at each profit center, the corporate goals become intertwined with the profit center's goals, strategies, and
objectives.

4. Corporate leadership must provide clear incentives and rewards for
managers and group officers who perform in intra-company competition based
on a system of weighted factors for long-term profitable growth.

5. Corporate yardsticks for investment in new equipment, facilities, market share, or acquisition of new product lines must be flexible to insure reception of all good ideas in diverse product growth areas.

6. The corporate office stimulates and aids profit centers through the following services: (a) A planning function that assists in defining strategies and tactics for five-year plans updated yearly, develops guidelines for investment in new products and markets, analyzes action programs, improves operational performance, and disciplines the organization to establish responsibilities and timetables to complete its plans. (b) Operations analysis, which provides a vehicle for interchange of knowhow, systems, and techniques among profit centers and provides objective outside viewpoints on procedures, processes, and organizational efficiencies. (c) Spin-off or disinvestment techniques for marginal products or operations. (d) Control of cash flow and motivation for maximum return of cash related to profitable growth. (e) Emphasis on management development and growth from within by requiring a management development program from each profit center and at every level of the corporate organizational structure.

Management Flexibility is Key

Just as human values are dynamic and subject to constant change, the values of a corporation are also dynamic. Even though we have seen the results of a specific management style and know that results have proven it to have been the right style for the right time, we must be willing to change our values and be ready and willing to adjust our management style when it becomes necessary. These adjustments may have to be revolutionary in some respects to the point where, in some instances, we may consolidate authority rather than delegate, as has been done in the past. I refer specifically to the role of the profit center manager. There are clear areas of coordination needed between profit centers in common product lines and with common customers. Further, there are obvious economies to be gained by pooling common requirements in transportation, distribution, service, and some areas of purchasing.

Since the highest product growth rate for the seventies will occur in the computer field and since all of you to some degree will be involved in the changing technology and automation techniques of EDP, we should mention a new management approach that has developed called "Leave the driving to us." It was prompted by the illusory "gifts" of the computer during the 1960's. There were great promises to management with little achievement. The biggest problem of the last decade and for the decade ahead is the "people" problem. Specifically, it is the shortage of qualified computer professionals. The shortage results in a 30% national turnover which results in even higher salary demands, continual training and indoctrination, and more importantly, management time that is being spent away from the primary business while in the quest for EDP people.

As a result, a new industry is springing up to serve the user — facilities management — or more descriptively, data resource management. This service provides an alternative to the traditional means of staffing the DP function one at a time ... through a single, pre-assembled package of people, machines, and technical expertise. It is important because of the peaks and valleys of DP skill requirements within a typical business firm. The data resource management company has a reservoir of skills from which to fill its clients' needs.

Even with this new concept the executive-technician gap lingers, although the data resource management firms are attempting to close that gap by teaching DP professionals to become businessmen. This should result in better communication between user and supplier. Further, the time that executives have to spend on the EDP peripheral specialty is reduced through data resource management and that time element becomes even more important with unbundling and the new requirement to buy software as well as hardware.

With every new concept there are attendant problems. In this case, they are:

1. Keeping the user involved and willing to further the use of EDP where provitable and practical.

2. Confidentiality of business data.

3. Fear of loss of control over a previously in-house function.

4. Keeping any savings intact; that is, insure that any savings are not illusory in nature.

5. How to contract for such services; for example, fixed price, time and material.

6. Problem of reindoctrinating new EDP vendor personnel to your business.

With each user the answers will be different. However, whatever the final result, one thing is already certain ... data resource management offers the computer user a powerful and welcome alternative.[7]

One of the businessman's major challenges of the 70's will be to automate the management information system. It is a new frontier in which businessmen can reduce costs dramatically and improve business perception, control, and judgement. Any operation with multiple plants and presently supporting a host of separate EDP facilities, each with its own computer personnel and programs, will be forced to evaluate the economies of regional computer and communication centers. The next 10 years will bring tremendous opportunities for automation of management information systems completely interrelating the production processes, product costs, and growth opportunities on a real time basis for management. Unfortunately, computer capabilities thus far have far outpaced our management perceptions of how best to maximize their effectiveness in our business plans and decision processes.

Education – An Opportunity

What is the role of business in manpower development? Over three years ago our company set forth in its long-range plans and strategies the objective to develop and participate in the growth market of "Private for Profit" schools. We believe there is a great need for good, vocational, technical and business schools that are job oriented. There are six million young people in our society between the ages of 18 and 21 who are not attending college, and 53% of each high school graduating class (a national average) is not college bound. Many school dropouts and high school graduates can neither afford the time nor the funds to go on for further general learning, and they need to be prepared specifically for business and technical opportunities which require specialized skills and are available in their local communities. In the next five years industry will need 350,000 new technicians, draftsmen, and designers; 138,000 new computer programmers and operators; 875,000 new secretaries and stenographers; and literally millions of clerks, bookkeepers, nurses, medical and dental assistants, and service employees.[8]

The business community spends billions of dollars each year in training, upgrading, and developing its employees. We believe that corporations should also contribute new directions and strengths to the management, curriculums, and training of our country's business and technical schools.

The process of training persons for a means of livelihood and re-training others for new career opportunities is certainly as important as the formal education itself. We recognize that as we continue to invest more dollars per worker, particularly in the new automation machines and processes,[9] one of the most limiting factors in our ability to properly utilize this

equipment is the number of skilled people who can operate the new computers, numerical control devices, and electronic systems controls. Unfortunately, in many instances it takes longer to train a person to understand
and handle automation equipment than it takes to manufacture that
equipment.

LSI now has 28 vocational schools and 14,000 students in 21 cities. We
are able to transfer new courses, open new markets, and develop needed
facilities by combining the strengths of these schools and by exchanging
ideas and opportunities.

One of the real assets of our job-oriented PFP schools is that each
student who enrolls does so because he thinks it is necessary in order to
make a living. He realizes that in the real world the personnel directors of
local industries must hire a specific skill, not just a degree. Over one-third
of the job applicants in the business community are not prepared for the
jobs they apply for and consequently have to be trained on the job by
industry. Unfortunately, there is little emphasis in our modern society on
the important part that craftsmen, technicians, skilled mechanics, and
business clerks play in our economic system.

The large majority of high-school seniors aspire to professional-level
jobs; yet, only ten percent of such job applicants entering the labor market
can be hired as professionals each year. Unfortunately, most parents, educators, and businessmen encourage Johnny and Jane to prepare for college
without evaluating their capabilities or the available opportunities in the
changing job market. A great challenge of the 70's would be for communities, in cooperation with educators and businessmen, to balance job skill
opportunities and educational training. As a result of such a job opportunity survey by the Chamber of Commerce of Greater Pittsburgh, Pennsyl-
vania, greater emphasis has been placed on vocational and technical
training for students in that area.

Even at the higher levels of college training, we are finding a new
relationship between educators and business. Dr. Norbert H. Hruby, president of Aquinas College in Grand Rapids, Michigan, has proposed to
interpose Aquinas College as a kind of *educational broker* for the business
community and groups of potential student/job applicants. To this end, an
industrial executive council made up of the top leaders of six Grand
Rapids businesses, plus the college president, will establish and implement
a program to meet the business needs of the community. Key technical
and professional personnel from business will assist in developing and

teaching the required courses and skills for these students. This is an exciting step in intertwining businessmen and educators in the complex subject of matching education and training with occupational needs in a community.

In any redistribution of our nation's resources, we must be concerned with the many side effects and impacts of the law of supply and demand. The inflationary effects of Medicare on our nation's health costs have been well documented in the last few years. Now we may expect some real changes in educational cost trends in the U.S. During the past ten years we have seen major growth in the use of federal funds to support education, and there is no question that this sector of our national priorities will continue to receive emphasis as noted by President Nixon's recent request for a National Institute of Education and the establishment of a National Student Loan Association. Federal funding has grown from a support level of one billion dollars in 1960 to eight billion dollars in 1970, covering education and manpower training programs in the federal government but not including the extensive training programs of the Department of Defense, Agriculture, Commerce, etc.[10] In addition, there are 2,139,000 loans and grants to students which are processed through the Office of Education and the Veterans Administration.[11] Student loans will be greatly expanded as a result of establishing the NSLA. What impact will this have on tuition costs and the growth of education facilities?[12]

There are over 700 PFP schools in the U.S. which are fulfilling a critical need in the vocational technical and business training area. Several hundred thousand students are taking job-oriented courses each year that are aimed at business and industry needs. At LSI we are strengthening our educational operations growth with new additions in the publishing and training fields. We have the will and the plans to be responsive in our educational efforts to the changing technology and automation developments of the seventies.

Where Do We Go From Here?

In closing, I would like to leave a challenge with this group. Surely all of us have profited greatly from the exchange of ideas . . . the viewpoints of education, business, labor, and government representatives . . . reflecting the current and future values of automation in our society. We have discussed the *management, attitudes,* and *responsibilities* related to automation. During all of these sessions, the one theme that kept recurring was — *What should we do about it?*

In this next decade, we will be in an era of great technological change and accordingly there is great concern for the implications of change to the total system. Therefore, let us try to manage it, rather than react on the basis of a crisis or expediency.

We have within the resources of this group the knowledge, tools, and capabilities to effectively plan a course of action that will be a tremendous force on those constraints that block effective utilization of our nation's resources. As a result of these past two and one half days of intensive dialogue, we have reached a consensus in many areas that there is need for action *now*. The answer to why we must act has been clearly established. Now let us determine what, by whom, where, and when.

As a first step in this venture, we should expand the scope of this symposium's purpose — that is, *establish our objectives* for managing change.

If we can agree on a list of objectives that are worthy of a planning effort, then we can proceed to the strategies and tactics for a successful course of action.

Each of you has given considerable thought to objectives you believe are needed in this technological era. As I review some of the objectives developed during this symposium, please think of them in the following perspective: — as a position paper; — as an education program; — as a coordinated effort by industry, labor, government, and education; — as a public affairs campaign; — as a proposal for national or state legislation. From these standpoints, the following ten suggested objectives are proposed for your consideration:

1. We believe we should improve and develop a more favorable climate for capital investment in the United States.

2. We believe it is desirable to seek price stability through sound fiscal and monetary policies of our government with a recognition of increased costs related to improvement in productivity.

3. We believe it is necessary to remove the constraints against automation in the field of housing.

4. We believe automation can make a greater contribution to the utilization of our resources in the medical and educational fields — i.e., EDP, television, technical assistants.

5. We believe that by greater cooperation between education, busi-

ness, and government, the transition phase from school to work can be greatly enhanced.

6. We believe that communities can greatly benefit by matching projected manpower needs with training courses for prospective job applicants.

7. We believe it is desirable to create an image of respect and dignity for the craftsmen, mechanics, clerks, and non-professionals who are essential to our labor force.

8. We believe it is of vital importance to undertake a method of properly evaluating, measuring, and comparing the productive output of the several service industries, government, and the education sector.

9. We believe it is critical that we encourage participative planning in establishing national goals with priorities. Further, we need to develop criteria for evaluation of the cost benefits in allocation of our nation's resources to the public sector.

10. We need to develop regional economic planning together with technological forecasts and assessments to insure that we conserve and maximize our resources with the least dislocation of our society and environment.

We have the opportunity now to participate in managing change through our combined efforts to shape, mold, and direct the forces of technology and automation in our society. Are we ready to leave the cloistered halls of debate and dialogue and advance into the arena to take action?

REFERENCES

1. Address of Attorney General John Mitchell before Georgia State Bar Association, June 6, 1969.
2. From $37.9 billion in 1969 – U.S. Department of Commerce.
3. *Automation Magazine,* January, 1970, page 63, "Government Influences Production Equipment Investment," Joel Barlow.
4. In the period from 1929 to 1947, business capital per worker did not increase and output per worker rose 1.5% a year. From 1947 to 1960, business capital per worker increased 50% and rate of output per worker increased 50% and rate of output per worker was almost double (2.8%) the prior period – *The Economy of the American People,* page 76.
5. MAPI – A Favorable Climate to Productive Investment – January 15, 1970, Charles W. Stewart.
6. Japan's GNP, which is already the second largest in the Free World, has in real terms averaged 12% per year for the past four years. The U.S. had a trade deficit with

Japan of $1.4 billion in 1969. International Commerce, March 16, 1970, Vol. 76, No. 11, page 2.

7. For a concise report on *"The economies of scale and computer peronnel"* which will affect the future plans of all business, state, local, and academic organizations, read Dr. Martin B. Solomon's article in *Datamation,* March, 1970.

8. Occupational employment patterns for 1960 and 1975, U.S. Department of Labor, Bureau of Labor Statistics.

9. Capital investment per worker increased 80% in the past ten years. Lionel D. Edie report, January 23, 1970.

10. MEL First National City Bank, New York City, February, 1970.

11. Budget of U.S. – U.S. Printing Office, Washington, D.C., 1969.

12. *A Review of Governmental Student Loan Programs* by Roger A. Freeman.

16

Technical Innovation: Key to Economic and Social Development

Roger W. Bolz

IN THE MYOPIC WORLD of the individual, it is almost axiomatic that technological advance is rampant on all fronts. Snatches of achievements in scattered areas bolstered by "amazing" feats in space, solid-state electronics and military weaponry solidify the basic impression.

Self-serving prognosticators inculate the idea that technology is in "a period of rapid and fantastic change." While some accomplishments certainly do border on what could be fairly labelled "fantastic" to the layman, in terms of economic and social development the idea is mostly myth.

The real pace of change, looking from the vantage point of personal and social benefits arising from advances in technology, is far more gradual than many would like to admit. In fact, it may be altogether too slow to help solve some of our most pressing problems in this major time of need.

Perhaps the most critical question facing us at present concerns the application of known technology — not new and as yet unknown techniques, but technical innovation in the solutions of current economic and social problems. And, in this regard, automation for business and industry assumes a leading position.

In spite of sophisticated definitions propounded by the "purists" to the contrary, automation that provides true economic and social benefits is founded on a solid base of mechanization. As a systems technology, no one facet can alone guarantee success anymore than a perfect brain can overcome the failure of the heart function in humans.

To use one industry as an example T.R. Schuerger[1] provides a keen insight from the standpoint of steelmaking with the observation that, "Automation is the process of making our environment more automatic.

Automation is of interest to manufacturing and processing industries because it has the potential to increase human productivity, to make hazardous operations safe for the human environment, and to regulate processes not readily comprehensible to humans in real time. Automation includes mechanization as well as the general aspects of instrumentation and control ... Modern systems concepts have extended the scope of automatic control from regulator and servo mechanisms concepts to those of integrated, combined, control functions. Integrated control is of interest, of course, because it alone provides the capability for automatic, real-time optimization of ... industry production complexes."

Obviously, the challenge is one of integrating largely known elements into new and more economically useful systems to serve the needs of mankind. The key is innovation with the stimulus of both need and desire for social betterment.

Redirection Is Needed

Ignorance and misinformation by fiction writers have conspired to create the great myth of vast technological change. Here, confusion of scientific discovery with technological innovation is the hard-core problem. New scientific knowledge of itself, like new technology, literally has no intrinsic value. Its transfer into useful end products and services will not take place automatically and from a study of the record, it most emphatically does not.

Is the great concern of the past decade with the march of the so-called "technological revolution" really valid? The answer must be, no. And, to again look at the record, it must be concluded that this concern should be redirected. The problem we face is not with any technological revolution, but rather with a revolution that did not take place.

There is a growing concern, evidenced by a growing body of literature, with the critical problem of technology transfer. Inherent values can only be realized when scientific and technological knowledge is put into useful form. Innovation is required to translate ideas into workable machinery and products. This is especially true of automation in manufacturing. Innovation is the key to practical success, yet appreciation of the systems technology involved and understanding of the basic requirements for successful adoption has been extremely slow in coming. For some companies, it has been too slow to preserve the business. With others, lack of appreciation has ended in expensive disasters that include inoperative systems, unsafe products, excessive operating costs, overproduction, uncontrolled quality, etc.

The Challenge of Change

Because this time gap between the discovery of new knowledge and its application is so great, there is good reason to examine the entire area. What has been learned? Can management speed up the transfer process? Is it possible to stimulate the innovative process and improve our economic and social development?

There is also good reason to make a serious effort to improve the process, for the record shows that otherwise the progress is dismally slow or almost nonexistent. As Lesher and Howick[2] comment, "A body of knowledge on how to accomplish this transfer has not yet been developed and assimilated."

Regardless of the situation of any particular organization today, it will and must face the challenge of change. Unless it is ready, one of the many facets that come with change will inevitably carry with it the seeds of failure.

Being ready to face the challenge daily, not merely accepting it but welcoming it and actively managing it favorably has major advantages. The most important obviously is survival..

Innovation to successfully cope with change is the major problem. General Motors' great innovator, Charles F. Kettering, pointed up the problem with his comment that, "The greatest durability contest in the world is trying to get a new idea into a factory." Success tends to create a strong adherence to the status quo, a complacency and a basic resistance to change, to new ideas.

Once the importance of innovation is recognized, there is the need to understand the key areas of activity. The usual conclusion is that the area of greatest need is for product innovation. Experience indicates this is not the case. The Advisory Panel of the Secretary of Commerce found that manufacturing engineering was the most important area of need in successful product development.[3] In the general product cost distribution it ranged from 40 to 60 percent of the total which also included advanced development, product design, start-up, and marketing.

A new product which cannot be produced in the required volume with the quality and price acceptable to the market will become nothing more than a statistic. Innovation can supply the needed solution to the problem.

Is Research Needed?

It is commonly accepted today that the key to new products and new processes is research and development. Discussion of the subject brings up visions of splendidly equipped laboratories with skilled teams of scientists and engineers working tirelessly to provide new, modern production techniques.

Belief is widespread that little is needed except large sums of money and well paid scientists to achieve amazing results. The record does not bear this out. In a study of 61 important developments made since 1900, only 11 could be traced to big research laboratories. Thirty-three were the work of independent inventors.

Research most certainly is needed. However, it must be good research that extends practical understanding of the important areas of manufacturing technology and the ability to achieve success with them. John R. Pierce, executive director of research-communications sciences division of Bell Telephone Labs., contends that research can be of value only when there are prople in the organization that are capable of using it effectively. Observes Pierce,[4] "The effective application of understanding and invention requires the effective and interrelated carrying out of many functions other than research, including development, trial, production, distribution, and continual evaluation and improvement."

What Pierce is making crystal clear is that knowledge for the sake of knowledge creates nothing. In the manufacturing sense automation is not automatically yours for the asking. And, ardent development of more and more sophisticated control systems, the ultimate answer in the eyes of some researchers, without concern for the other basic elements in the total manufacturing cycle, is the path to "economic nowhere."

As concludes Daniel V. DeSimone, director of the Office of Invention and Innovation of NBS, "The successful innovator or inventor needs a conventionless mind stored with the relevant technology and scientific principles, and exercised in the techniques of retrieving the relevant and discarding the unnecessary. He must have knowledge coupled with a free-wheeling imaginativeness." Such innovation is the most important element in the creation of economically significant contributions to automation technology or, for that matter, any technology that leads to economic and social improvement.

Is the Technology Available?

Under the erroneous contention that automation is a specific package of "this" or "that," most manufacturers take little interest in understanding the technology. For a fact, the technology is available but certainly not as any specific package. The most electrifying results are attained primarily through what could be classed as an extraordinary insight into the problem at hand coupled with creation of an engineering solution from rather ordinary and available technology.

The evolution of a "total manufacturing system" concept capable of being executed into a practical profitable installation entails a high degree of innovation. There is no question that the technology very largely is available but its transfer into useful equipment via innovation is the problem.

"The real barriers," in the words of Dr. Charles Kimball,[5] "are neither financial nor technical. The barriers are outdated institutional practice, lack of entrepreneurship, and of reluctance to accept new ideas and new practices." Kimball sees the major barriers to adaptation of new technology in corporate managements' unwillingness to take risks, the absence of any preparation for the changes created by new processes, a wedded familiarity with the present methods, concentration on the short term vs. the long term attainments, and finally just plain lack of knowledge.

With the automation of manufacturing operations, although the technology is available, the parochial approach of most managements guarantees either minimal success in terms of the possible or none at all. Unless the problem is approached as a total system the benefits possible at one stage may be inaccessible because of changes needed at some other stage. Success of any process as an automated entity usually depends upon the integration of elements in several stages simultaneously.

The Problem of Transfer

Obviously, even though the necessary technology is available, it can offer little other than a curiosity if it is not put to use. What insures advantageous use? Certainly not mere availability. Project Hindsight a study made by the Department of Defense,[6] concluded that: ". . . it tells us once again that recognized need is the key to efficient utilization. But to recognize need one has to have very detailed knowledge of either a class of systems or a specific system so that the critical problems can be addressed."

The problem of transfer is readily recognized from the comment in Section 6 of Project Hindsight's report: "A utilized innovation can occur only when there is a conjunction of three elements; (1) a recognized need; (2) competent people with relevant scientific or technological ideas and (3) financial support."

Thus it is that scientists can discover or unearth new knowledge but, unfortunately, scientists are not innovators. In the same vein, neither are companies or government agencies. In the words of John R. Platt,[7] "They all shrink, like other men, from unheard-of projects for which there is no precedent, even obvious and important projects, because they are afraid they will be laughed at or cut off from support."

The problem is no small one for good reasons. Innovation is not mere simple invention or just research and development. Innovation involves much more than the conception of the idea or basic invention. It involves in addition the introduction of the process or product into the economy — the recognition and adaptation of an idea in order that it results in true economic advantages. A National Planning Association Study[8] analyzing 560 innovations showed this to be the case with two thirds of the total.

Because of the many restraints on introducing innovation, technological advance is slower by far than the available knowledge would indicate. Mansfield[9] indicates that the much publicized expenditures in R&D and the published data greatly exaggerate the rate of advance in innovation.

Mansfield postulated these four major reasons for restraints on diffusion of innovation: (1) Only as the number of firms in an industry adopting an innovation increases, does the probability of its adoption by a nonuser increase; (2) The expected profitability of its adoption; (3) For equally profitable innovations, the probability of adoption tends to be smaller for innovations requiring relatively large investments, and (4) The probability of adoption of an innovation is dependent on the industry in which the innovation is introduced. Secondary reasons he lists as: (1) If an innovation displaces very durable equipment, the probability of its adoption is lessened; (2) The probability of adoption will be higher in firms that are expanding at a relatively rapid rate; and (3) All other factors being equal, the probability of the adoption of an innovation increases with time.

Within any particular firm certain key factors can influence or delay the introduction of new innovative technology. These can be listed as the size of the firm, the general attitude and intellectual orientation of management the expectation of early profit from the innovation, the rate of growth of the company, the firm's current cash flow, the age of the industry and/or the management personnel, the complexity of the innovation, and the general trend of profitability or competition being experienced.

From careful study of the process of innovation it can be concluded quite readily that it is to a singular degree an individual activity calling for concentrated leadership. DeSimone of NBS contends[10] it calls for outstandingly creative individuals who fit G.B. Shaw's definition of "unreasonable men."

Dr. J. Herbert Hollomon, former Assistant Secretary of Commerce for Science and Technology, has made the pointed conclusion about this problem of introducing innovation[11] that, "Our real secret in this country is the fact that a young fellow has a chance to go out and start a new small business on his own without having to work through established organizations or the conservative constituencies."

Obviously, then, the introduction of a technological approach as basically innovative as automation follows a similar pattern. Barring those developments such as computers and numerical control, where government stimulus created the market demand, what conditions open the doors of industry to automation? Again, as Mansfield postulates, they are to an amazing degree economic. We must conclude from study ranging over years of successful activity that over 90 percent fall into one of these categories:

1. Companies that could not conceivably manufacture their product in sufficient quantity to satisfy their market demand without automation.

2. Companies whose products could not conceivably be produced at all without automation.

3. Companies whose products could not be sold competitively without utilizing automation.

The need is growing. Innovative manufacturing automation will become imperative to the survival of many companies pressed by today's stringent social demands. Is it possible to do more about the introduction of new innovative ideas in manufacturing operations? What should the forward-looking company be doing?

Can Technical Innovation Be Managed?

Where technical innovation is concerned, most companies become trapped in a conflict of policy and practice. Donald A. Schon has observed,[12] "It is company policy to seek innovation, and company practice (often for the best of reasons) to resist it." As a result, it becomes imperative for management to become personally involved. All company activities can and do lead to innovation, but it requires executive decision and wisdom to obtain the benefits available.

Entrepreneurial skill is the crucial factor in the innovation process. It is necessary to see the possibilities and, in effect, commit present resources to future expectations rather than facts. Creative management is desirable and necessary since,[13] "Innovation is purposeful, organized, risk-taking change introduced for the purpose of satisfying wants and resulting in increased profitability. It means not only adapting to new conditions but creating new conditions; and it is important in policies, goals, organization, marketing, and communications as it is in the technological areas of product and process."

Innovation can be managed to the real benefit of any company.[14] It requires a systematic approach which includes use of a planning discipline for present operations and continuing reappraisal of the business and the direction it should be taking. It should be recognized that good corporate planning comprises use of the company's resources and talents to the most profitable ends for both the customer and the company. "Innovation is at the core of such planning for change," concludes the ACME.[13]

Essential steps recommended by ACME include a vigorous company program to promote innovations generally and effective means to make individual effort useful. These recommendations should be seriously considered:

1. Set goals that management must stretch for. In the words of Frederick R. Kappel, former president of AT&T, "... the genius of the goal-setter is the ability to distinguish between the possible and the impossible — but be willing to get very close to the latter."

2. Keep policy statements fresh. The same old words rapidly become stale and lose their meaning. Stimulating new restatement is a must.

3. Support vigorous research efforts. Aggressive research effort should be promoted and rewarded.

4. Communicate the right image. Both the inside and outside world should know the company's policies to attract new talent and as well hold the old.

5. Employ management R&D. Lengthen the arm and thrust of key managers through stimulating investigation and aid in management methods.

6. Set up executive task forces to examine key problems. Charge the groups to really raise the questions of how, why, what. Provide firm backing as problems will invariably move across pet corporate preserves.

7. Promote aggressive young managers into top ranks of the company. The spur to innovate dies out as officers grow older. New values can be gained from new thinking.

8. Appoint a Vice President in Charge of Innovation. An executive of broad background and creativeness can stir up a tremendous amount of change merely by challenging current policies and practices.

9. Establish a permanent idea group. In lieu of a one-man effort this concept involves an executive group charged with challenging present efforts and directing thinking into new paths. Such an organized operation is required to overcome resistance present in many firms.

Not only can innovation be managed; it must be managed if the company expects to compete and remain on the scene. To wait for innovation to take place is at best hazardous.

To create the necessary climate for advance, the individual manager must believe firmly in innovation and in risk-taking. As in the old adage, nothing ventured, nothing gained. He must ask for and stimulate thinking in this direction recognizing full well that in so doing he will be unpopular with many who consider this as "rocking the boat."

Industrial management must ask questions such as these[15] in their quest for new directions:

1. Are we making a serious attempt to understand the major impacts and effects of broad technological change in the economy, business, government, and society? Are we concentrating our attention on those

technical innovations which may stimulate economic growth in our company? In our industry?

2. Are we making a systematic effort to take full advantage of technological advances and new ways of doing things that could reduce our costs and increase our manufacturing effectiveness?

3. Are we aware of the total impact that automation will have on our business and are we preparing for it?

4. Have we created a positive climate for improved economic performance throughout our company?

One final conclusion can be made: Unless management understands the implications of automation technology in terms of a total manufacturing systems concept it will be hard pressed to compete in future markets. The economic effects on the company and their social repercussions as a result can be long range and serious. On the other hand, a positive attitude can provide new and dynamic aspects to any organization and the economy as a whole. In a study of the Japanese scene, Philip M. Boffey[16] highlights the case with the conclusion that, ". . . while American firms have led the world in original innovation over the past 15 or 20 years, Japanese firms have been the most successful at adopting and diffusing new techniques and products. Interestingly enough, the study concluded that performance in originating inventions did not seem to affect a nation's overall economic growth, but performance in the diffusion of technological innovations did seem to be associated with economic growth."

Are You a Champion?

Where an organized approach simply cannot be used, or where competitive pressures make a leisurely attack on the problem impractical, another useful method can be employed. Be a "Champion" or put the job into the hands of a "Champion" and provide him with firm backing.

The Champion is needed to fight for innovation throughout the entire corporate system. Obviously, he must have considerable power and prestige in the organization in order to be effective. Because of the risks involved and the importance of the goals being sought, management must become deeply involved in the innovative processes that alone can lead to successful automation that really benefits everyone.

One authority, experienced in the broad requirements of introducing computerized process control into an old-line industry, described the successful Champion as a "tiger." Today, for many companies, to accept anything less is flirting with catastrophe.

The tiger will create friction in his introduction of new concepts. Changes of any kind, much less the changes of automating, create difficulties with complacent personnel intent on grinding out what is classed as merely "acceptable" product for managers who put rules ahead of results, dote on a "taut ship," "teamwork," "committee decisions," and the like. But the relatively minor upheaval involved with improvement avoids the economic and social price paid for tranquility which Leo Cherne[17] summarizes as ". . . the things that don't get started, the breakthroughs and the innovations and the creative new leaps that just do not take place."

Management must champion the Champion. But in so doing, they must also insure that innovation is economically oriented, practical and realistic. In any workable program both must avoid at all costs common problems such as these that invariably result in costly failures:

1. Unrealistic assessment of the technological possibilities.

2. Admiration of complex rather than simple solutions.

3. Conversion of specialties into independent disciplines for their own sakes.

4. Confusion of scientific information with technological innovation.

5. Inability to recognize the relative importance and complementary character of manufacturing research and product research.

Conclusions

Economically as well as socially significant industrial achievement requires enterprising, creative ventures based on carefully evaluated and calculated probabilities. But somehow, when the question is raised, "Who champions automation in your company?" answers rather foreign to the entrepreneur seem to predominate. The situation unfortunately resolves itself into some moribund practices depending completely on suppliers for more efficient equipment, refusing to invest in legitimate automation development where such effort is obviously valuable, or waiting for someone else to carry out the research necessary to bring new automated production systems into being. Most commonly, it devolves into a pointless debate involving esoteric definitions of just what constitutes automation.

Advancing technology and the multiplying complexity of modern automated production systems have made such practices by management increasingly expensive, and now often disastrous. The luxury of waiting for the competition to solve problems has become dangerous; and few equipment suppliers have the incentive or the ability to risk the increasingly larger investments needed.

Are you providing your manufacturing and process engineering teams with the critical tools needed for insuring profitable operations? Is your manufacturing research and development program exploiting innovation so as to create a bulwark against the competition ahead?

Only financially and socially responsible management can spark the creative efforts of the corporate staff. Have you asked some of these important questions to learn where you stand in the competitive picture?

Where throughout the world do you find the most advanced manufacturing methods of your industry?

Where do you look for information and capabilities of automated production applicable to your operations?

How do you compare, in reality, with other industries having comparable products and production methods?

Where did the newest most advanced manufacturing systems and operations used in your area of industry today originate? Here or abroad? By what means were they brought to fruition?

A thorough study for answers to these questions will reveal some interesting facts. The problem is not so much one of management accepting innovation as it is of recognizing that keeping competitive demands innovation with a broad outlook and new perspective. Progress always involves risk and enterprise; acceptance of change. Not all profitable improvements require big, expensive changes. Mostly, the significant returns are found where new ideas can take root and find nourishment. There must be insatiable curiosity and an open door. Because the problems accumulated from past practice are legion; the call to action is clear and impelling.

REFERENCES

1. Schuerger, T.R., "Automatic Control in the Steel Industry – A challenge for the Future," Proceedings of the 19th International ISA Iron and Steel Instrumentation Symposium, March 17-19, 1969, Pittsburgh, Pa.

2. Lesher, Richard L., and George J. Howick, "Assessing Technology Transfer," Scientific and Technical Information Div., NASA, Washington, D.C., 1966.

3. "Technological Innovation: Its Environments and Management," Government Printing Office, Washington, D.C. 20402.

4. Pierce, John R., "When Is Research The Answer?", *Science,* Volume 159, Page 1079.

5. Lesher, op. cit.

6. "Project Hindsight," Chalmers W. Sherwin and Raymond S. Isenson, *Science,* Volume 156, Page 1571.

7. Platt, John R., "Diversity," *Science,* Volume 154, Page 1132.

8. National Planning Association, *Looking Ahead,* February 1967.

9. National Science Foundation, *Reviews of Data on Research & Development.*

10. De Simone, Daniel V., "The Innovator," *Engineer,* January-February 1967, Page 8.

11. Technology and World Trade, Proceedings of a Symposium, November 16-17, 1966. National Bureau of Standards Miscellaneous Publication 284, U.S. Government Printing Office, Washington, D.C.

12. Schon, Donald A., "Six Ways to Strangle Innovation," *Think,* July-August 1963, Page 29.

13. "Management of Innovation – Key to the Future,"*Management Consultant,* publication of the Association of Consulting Management Engineers, Inc., New York. 1962 Series Number 1, 1965 Series Number 2.

14. Buchanan, Paul C., "Innovative Organizations – A Study in Organization Development," Monograph on Applying Behavioural Science Research in Industry, Industrial Relations Counselors, Inc., 1964, Page 87.

15. "Manufacturing and the Challenge of Technology," *Industrial Management,* November 1967, Page 11.

16. Philip M. Boffey, "Japan: Industrial Research Struggles to Close the Gap." *Science,* Volume 167, January 16, 1970, Page 265.

17. Cherne, Leo, "The Era of the Uncommon Man,"*Personnel,* November-December, 1965, Page 17.

About the Authors

Frederick L. Bates: The Head of the Department of Sociology and Anthropology, University of Georgia, Athens, Georgia. BA, MA, Sociology, the George Washington University; Ph.D, Sociology, the University of North Carolina. Dr. Bates' principal interests lie in social structure and social change, themes that are related in a number of his books and articles; the most recent, a monograph entitled "The Structure of Occupations."

Gordon B. Carson: Vice President for Business and Finance, the Ohio State University, Columbus, Ohio 43210. BSME, D. Eng., Case Institute of Technology, MSME, ME, Yale University; also attended the University of Michigan. Dr. Carson directed research which led to electrical controls on automatic screw machines and the development of die casting equipment. An innovator in the automation of the shoe manufacturing process, he also helped develop protective headgear for the U.S. Air Force. Mr. Carson edits The Production Handbook and has written papers dealing with atmospheric and water pollution, traffic and parking, and citizen participation in democratic government. Dr. Carson is also Vice President and Chairman of the Advisory Council for the Center for the Study of Automation and Society.

Melvyn R. Copen: Associate Dean for Graduate Studies, College of Business Administration, University of Houston, Houston, Texas 77004. BS, MS, Massachusetts Institute of Technology; DBA, Harvard Business School. At one time worked to establish a graduate school of business and taught production management as consultant to the Ford Foundation in New Delhi, India. Dr. Copen's primary interests involve the introduction of change and its effect on society. Research interests are concerned with problems of introducing effective managerial practices in developing nations, the impact of advanced industrial technology on the management of the individual firm, and the general trend of values and activities in society as a whole. Dr. Copen is in Washington for the 1970-'71 academic year serving as White House Fellow. Dr. Copen is a member of the Advisory Council for the Center for the Study of Automation and Society.

K. Robert Hahn: Senior Vice President, Lear-Siegler, Inc., 3171 South Bundy Drive, Santa Monica, California 90406. BA, Oberlin College; LLD Cornel University. Member of the bar, Washington, D.C. and Michigan. General counsel and secretary for Lake Central Airlines; manager government contracts, Lear, Inc.; v.p. and director military sales, Lear, Inc.; executive vice president and director, Lear, Inc.; president,

Power Equipment Division of Lear-Siegler, Inc.; served as fighter pilot and instructor in the U.S. Air Force during World War II. Mr. Hahn is a member of the Board of Trustees for the Center for the Study of Automation and Society.

Joseph Harrington, Jr.: Management Consultant, formerly with Arthur D. Little, Inc., Cambridge, Massachusetts. BS and Sc.D. in Mechanical Engineering from the Massachusetts Institute of Technology. Before joining ADL in 1955, Dr. Harrington was Assistant Director of Research for the United Shoe Machinery Corporation where his work included research programming, product diversification, market analysis and design, and development of automatic machinery. He joined Arthur D. Little, Inc. in 1955 where he organized and directed work in mechanical engineering. He has lectured to many professional societies and trade associations on the subject of automation and mechanization. These lectures have covered both the technical aspects of capital equipment development, and the socioeconomic impact of such machines.

Russell A. Hedden: Executive Vice President – Automotive and Automation Div., Bendix Corp., Southfield, Michigan 48075. Engineering graduate of the Newark (N.J.) College of Engineering, Mr. Hedden draws on over 30 years of experience in industrial management in presenting his views on the attitudes of management towards automation in the 1970's. He has specialized in this aspect of industrial management since joining Bendix in 1962, and has often spoken on the social and economic gains made possible by increased automation of production processes.

James C. Hetrick: Management Consultant, Concord, Massachusetts. B.Sc. Philadelphia College of Pharmacy & Science; M.Sc. University of Delaware. Formerly with the Ethyl Corporation, Continental Oil Company, and most recently, Arthur D. Little, Inc., Mr. Hetrick has worked in operations research and mathematical modeling of production scheduling, inventory control systems, physical distribution, research direction and technological forecasting, capital budgeting, risk analysis, long range planning, and economic development programs.

George Kozmetsky: Dean of the College of Business Administration and of the Graduate School of Business, The University of Texas at Austin. Dr. Kozmetsky is a former faculty member of the University of Washington, Harvard Graduate School of Business Administration, and the Graduate School of Industrial Administration at Carnegie-Mellon University. In 1952, Dr. Kozmetsky joined Hughes Aircraft Company. He moved to Litton Industries in 1954, where he became vice president. With another Litton associate he founded in 1960 Teledyne, Inc. Dr. Kozmetsky continues as a director and consultant to Teledyne, Inc.; acts as a consultant to the Administrator of NASA; is the author of several books and articles covering his pioneering research in management sciences, automation, and man-machine methodology.

John J. McNiff: Subsequent to the Symposium, Mr. McNiff died from injuries received in an automobile accident in the Washington area. Mr. McNiff was President of the International Economic Consultants Corporation and had extensive experience in all phases of economic and social programs from planning and systems design, to project administration and evaluation. He served as a member of the Committee on Foreign Labor Conditions, U.S. Department of Labor; as a technical representative of the Office of the Special Representative for Trade Negotiations, Executive Office of the President; as a member of the National Advisory Committee of the National Council of Senior Citizens; as special advisor to the New York City "Mayor's Committee on Exploitation of Workers;" as a member of the American delegation at the Organization of Economic Cooperation and Development Paris seminar on industrial democracy and as a member of the American delegation at the Anglo-American Conference on the "Social and Economic Consequences of Automation" and at the Anglo-American-Canadian Conferences on the "Impact of Automation and Technological Change on Trade Union Interests and Policies" which were convened by the Ditchley Foundation at Oxfordshire, England.

John E. Mock: Director of the Georgia Science and Technology Commission, Atlanta, Georgia 30332. B.S., M.S., Ph.D., Purdue University; MBA, The George Washington University. Taught advanced mathematics at the University of Virginia, The George Washington University and the U.S. Air Force Academy. He has over 20 years experience as a science administrator in the federal government, primarily in the office of the Secretary of Defense, and several years in state government, in the Office of the Governor. He serves as Atomic Energy Coordinator for the State of Georgia, as a member of the Georgia Economic Development Policy Council, as Director of the Georgia Institute for Research in Bio-Technology, as Director pro tem of the Coastal States Organization, and as Co-Chairman of the Governor's Council for Science and Technology in Society. He is the author of over 100 papers on space science, civil defense, operations research, systems analysis, health science, radiation safety, and science policy. In 1960, Dr. Mock was the recipient of the Mark Mills Award of the American Nuclear Society for his theoretical and experimental work in nuclear science.

Herbert W. Robinson: Business Consultant, Suite 406, 1015 – 18th Street, N.W., Washington, D.C. 20036. University College, Hull, England, B.Sc. (Econ.); London School of Economics, Ph.D., (Econ.); Balliol College, Oxford, England, D. Phil. A native of England, Dr. Robinson earned Ph.D's in economics and mathematical statistics from the London School of Economics and Balliol College, Oxford. He then embarked on a career in economic and financial administration. He was in the British Cabinet Office as assistant to Lord Cherwell, Scientific and Statistical Advisor to Prime Minister Churchill. He has held important posts with the British and U.S. Governments, United Nations, and World Bank. He came to U.S. in 1943, became a citizen in 1948. In 1954, he was principal founder of CEIR, Inc., a computer software and service bureau company, serving as company Chairman and President for 14 years. Following the merger of CEIR into Control Data Corporation, Dr. Robinson served as a Vice President and member of the Executive Council of Control Data. Dr. Robinson is a member of the Advisory Council of the Center for the Study of Automation and Society.

Ben B. Seligman: Professor of Economics and Director, Labor Relations and Research Center, University of Massachusetts, Amherst, Massachusetts 01002. Visiting Professor, Heller Graduate School, Brandeis University. Formerly Director of Research, Retail Clerks International Association, Associate Fellow, Institute for Policy Studies, lecturer in economics, Brooklyn College. Author of seven books on economic theory, poverty, automation and business history. Contributor of more than 100 papers, articles and reviews to professional and other journals. President,

Association for Evolutionary Economics; executive board, Industrial Relations Research Association. Guggenheim Fellow, 1967; Distinguished Alumnus Award of Honor, Brooklyn College, 1968.

Joseph B. Warren: Colonel, United States Air Force, Deputy Comptroller for Data Automation, Office of the Secretary of Defense, Pentagon Building, Washington, D.C. B.S., University of Maryland. Col. Warren is presently responsible for policies, criteria and standards governing selection, acquisition, use and management of automatic data processing equipment in the Department of Defense, the Department of Defense Data Element and Codes Standardization Program, and the design, development and implementation of computer based information systems for the Office of the Secretary of Defense. He wrote "Financial Management in the Air Force Ballistic Systems Comand," and "Command and Control Versus Management Information."

Edgar Weinberg: Deputy Assistant Commissioner for Productivity and Technology U.S. Department of Labor, Washington, D.C. Mr. Weinberg attended College of the City of New York and has a graduate degree from American University. He has worked in various government agencies. He has written on impact of technological change for Monthly Labor Review, Advanced Management, Encyclopedia of Education and other publications. He has developed and teaches a new course on Technological Change and Manpower at the George Washington University. Mr. Weinberg is a member of the Advisory Council for the Center for the Study of Automation and Society.

Appendix

Center for the Study of Automation and Society
P.O. Box 47, Athens, Georgia 30601
Telephone: (404) 542-4718

The Center for the Study of Automation and Society is a non-profit corporation headquartered in the College of Business Administration at the University of Georgia in Athens, but involving personnel and resources from many universities, corporations, associations and agencies with which relationships are maintained. The mission of the Center is to serve the interests of business, industry, labor, education, government and other organizations to the common effort to develop automation with full awareness of its social implications.

Center Objectives

Encourage and develop resources for planning and analysis.

Disseminate general knowledge of automation as a technology and its social implications.

Supply specific data needed for planning and decision-making.

Develop actual working relationships among industry, labor, education and government.

Involve professional resources of universities, corporations, unions and government agencies.

Explore applications of automation for economic development within and among nations.

Study the environmental impact of automation as a technology.